MW00640030

MOSES

DISCOVER GOD'S FAITHFULNESS
ON LIFE'S JOURNEY

MARK
RASMUSSEN

Copyright © 2014 by Striving Together Publications. All Scripture quotations are taken from the King James Version.

First published in 2014 by Striving Together Publications, a ministry of Lancaster Baptist Church, Lancaster, CA 93535. Striving Together Publications is committed to providing tried, trusted, and proven books that will further equip local churches to carry out the Great Commission. Your comments and suggestions are valued.

All rights reserved. No part of this book may be reproduced, stored in a retrieval system, or transmitted in any form or by any means—electronic, mechanical, photocopy, recording, or otherwise—without written permission of the publisher, except for brief quotations in printed reviews.

Striving Together Publications
4020 E. Lancaster Blvd.
Lancaster, CA 93535
800.201.7748

Cover design by Andrew Jones
Layout by Craig Parker
Edited by David Coon, Penny Edmonds, and Melodie Workman
Special thanks to our proofreaders

ISBN 978-1-59894-275-0
Printed in the United States of America

Table of Contents

Moses in the Palace
Learning to Honor God

Text

EXODUS 1:8–2:15

8   *Now there arose up a new king over Egypt, which knew not Joseph.*

9   *And he said unto his people, Behold, the people of the children of Israel are more and mightier than we:*

10   *Come on, let us deal wisely with them; lest they multiply, and it come to pass, that, when there falleth out any war, they join also unto our enemies, and fight against us, and so get them up out of the land.*

11   *Therefore they did set over them taskmasters to afflict them with their burdens. And they built for Pharaoh treasure cities, Pithom and Raamses.*

12   *But the more they afflicted them, the more they multiplied and grew. And they were grieved because of the children of Israel.*

13   *And the Egyptians made the children of Israel to serve with rigour:*

14   *And they made their lives bitter with hard bondage, in morter, and in brick, and in all manner of service in the field: all their service, wherein they made them serve, was with rigour.*

15   *And the king of Egypt spake to the Hebrew midwives, of which the name of the one was Shiphrah, and the name of the other Puah:*

16   *And he said, When ye do the office of a midwife to the Hebrew women, and see them upon the stools; if it be a son, then ye shall kill him: but if it be a daughter, then she shall live.*

17   But the midwives feared God, and did not as the king of Egypt commanded them, but saved the men children alive.

18   And the king of Egypt called for the midwives, and said unto them, Why have ye done this thing, and have saved the men children alive?

19   And the midwives said unto Pharaoh, Because the Hebrew women are not as the Egyptian women; for they are lively, and are delivered ere the midwives come in unto them.

20   Therefore God dealt well with the midwives: and the people multiplied, and waxed very mighty.

21   And it came to pass, because the midwives feared God, that he made them houses.

22   And Pharaoh charged all his people, saying, Every son that is born ye shall cast into the river, and every daughter ye shall save alive.

2:1   And there went a man of the house of Levi, and took to wife a daughter of Levi.

2   And the woman conceived, and bare a son: and when she saw him that he was a goodly child, she hid him three months.

3   And when she could not longer hide him, she took for him an ark of bulrushes, and daubed it with slime and with pitch, and put the child therein; and she laid it in the flags by the river's brink.

4   And his sister stood afar off, to wit what would be done to him.

5   And the daughter of Pharaoh came down to wash herself at the river; and her maidens walked along by the river's side; and when she saw the ark among the flags, she sent her maid to fetch it.

6   And when she had opened it, she saw the child: and, behold, the babe wept. And she had compassion on him, and said, This is one of the Hebrews' children.

7   Then said his sister to Pharaoh's daughter, Shall I go and call to thee a nurse of the Hebrew women, that she may nurse the child for thee?

8   And Pharaoh's daughter said to her, Go. And the maid went and called the child's mother.

9   And Pharaoh's daughter said unto her, Take this child away, and nurse it for me, and I will give thee thy wages. And the woman took the child, and nursed it.

10   And the child grew, and she brought him unto Pharaoh's daughter, and he became her son. And she called his name Moses: and she said, Because I drew him out of the water.

11   And it came to pass in those days, when Moses was grown, that he went out unto his brethren, and looked on their burdens: and he spied an Egyptian smiting an Hebrew, one of his brethren.

12   And he looked this way and that way, and when he saw that there was no man, he slew the Egyptian, and hid him in the sand.

13   And when he went out the second day, behold, two men of the Hebrews strove together: and he said to him that did the wrong, Wherefore smitest thou thy fellow?

14   And he said, Who made thee a prince and a judge over us? intendest thou to kill me, as thou killedst the Egyptian? And Moses feared, and said, Surely this thing is known.

15   Now when Pharaoh heard this thing, he sought to slay Moses. But Moses fled from the face of Pharaoh, and dwelt in the land of Midian: and he sat down by a well.

Overview

As we travel through the life of Moses, we will learn that those who *honor* God will be *honored by* God. Having received the best education available, Moses was being groomed for Egyptian royalty and would grow into a strong-willed and powerful man whom God would use mightily. The day came when Moses faced a crossroad, and at this crucial juncture, he chose to take his stand with his own people—the people of God.

Introduction

_____

_____

_____

PHILIPPIANS 4:13

13   I can do all things through Christ which strengtheneth me.

1 JOHN 4:4

4   Ye are of God, little children, and have overcome them: because greater is he that is in you, than he that is in the world.

I. _____ by God (2:1–2:9)

A. *His parents _____ God (2:1–4).*

ROMANS 12:1–2

1   I beseech you therefore, brethren, by the mercies of God, that ye present your bodies a living sacrifice, holy, acceptable unto God, which is your reasonable service.

2   And be not conformed to this world: but be ye transformed by the renewing of your mind, that ye may prove what is that good, and acceptable, and perfect, will of God.

PSALM 127:3

3   Lo, children are an heritage of the LORD: and the fruit of the womb is his reward.

B. *His parents were honored _____ (2:5–9).*

HEBREWS 11:6, 23

6   But without faith it is impossible to please him: for he that cometh to God must believe that he is, and that he is a rewarder of them that diligently seek him.

23   By faith Moses, when he was born, was hid three months of his parents, because they saw he was a proper child; and they were not afraid of the king's commandment.

JUDE 22

22   And of some have compassion, making a difference:

PROVERBS 11:18

18   The wicked worketh a deceitful work: but to him that soweth righteousness shall be a sure reward.

REVELATION 22:12

12   And, behold, I come quickly; and my reward is with me, to give every man according as his work shall be.

II. _____ for Royalty (2:10)

A. *He was brought in by _____*
    (2:10a).

PROVERBS 21:1

1   The king's heart is in the hand of the LORD, as the rivers of water: he turneth it whithersoever he will.

B. *He was brought up by the _____*
    (2:10b).

ACTS 7:21–22

21   And when he was cast out, Pharaoh's daughter took him up, and nourished him for her own son.

22 And Moses was learned in all the wisdom of the Egyptians, and was mighty in words and in deeds.

1 CORINTHIANS 6:19–20

19 What? know ye not that your body is the temple of the Holy Ghost which is in you, which ye have of God, and ye are not your own?

20 For ye are bought with a price: therefore glorify God in your body, and in your spirit, which are God's.

III. _____ to His People (2:11–15)

A. He was willing to _____ the palace (2:11).

HEBREWS 11:24–27

24 By faith Moses, when he was come to years, refused to be called the son of Pharaoh's daughter;

25 Choosing rather to suffer affliction with the people of God, than to enjoy the pleasures of sin for a season;

26 Esteeming the reproach of Christ greater riches than the treasures in Egypt: for he had respect unto the recompence of the reward.

27 By faith he forsook Egypt, not fearing the wrath of the king: for he endured, as seeing him who is invisible.

B. He was willing to _____ his people (2:11–15).

PHILIPPIANS 2:4

4 Look not every man on his own things, but every man also on the things of others.

Conclusion

Study Questions

1. Describe God's intervention in the birth and survival of Moses.

2. For what purpose did Pharaoh's daughter have Moses educated by the Egyptians?

3. What prompted Moses to commit murder?

4. What was Pharaoh's reaction to Moses' killing the Egyptian?

5. In what miraculous ways has God intervened in your life, perhaps keeping you from serious harm or death?

6.   What opportunities is God giving you now to learn and grow in your Christian life, and how are you taking advantage of them?

7.   What opportunities has God given you lately to be a special help and encouragement to others?

8.   Describe a time in your life that you considered to be a setback or a tragedy, but now you can see how God has used it to help you fulfill His will.

Memory Verses

HEBREWS 11:24–25

24   By faith Moses, when he was come to years, refused to be called the son of Pharaoh's daughter;
25   Choosing rather to suffer affliction with the people of God, than to enjoy the pleasures of sin for a season;

Moses in the Desert
Developing a Genuine Walk with God

Text

EXODUS 2:11–19

11 *And it came to pass in those days, when Moses was grown, that he went out unto his brethren, and looked on their burdens: and he spied an Egyptian smiting an Hebrew, one of his brethren.*

12 *And he looked this way and that way, and when he saw that there was no man, he slew the Egyptian, and hid him in the sand.*

13 *And when he went out the second day, behold, two men of the Hebrews strove together: and he said to him that did the wrong, Wherefore smitest thou thy fellow?*

14 *And he said, Who made thee a prince and a judge over us? intendest thou to kill me, as thou killedst the Egyptian? And Moses feared, and said, Surely this thing is known.*

15 *Now when Pharaoh heard this thing, he sought to slay Moses. But Moses fled from the face of Pharaoh, and dwelt in the land of Midian: and he sat down by a well.*

16 *Now the priest of Midian had seven daughters: and they came and drew water, and filled the troughs to water their father's flock.*

17 *And the shepherds came and drove them away: but Moses stood up and helped them, and watered their flock.*

18 *And when they came to Reuel their father, he said, How is it that ye are come so soon to day?*

19 *And they said, An Egyptian delivered us out of the hand of the shepherds, and also drew water enough for us, and watered the flock.*

Overview

There is no substitute for time spent alone with God. In quiet times, away from distractions and the busyness of life, God can truly speak to us and help us become more of what He wants us to be.

Introduction

_____

_____

_____

I. Moses Was _____

PSALM 142:4–5

4 *I looked on my right hand, and beheld, but there was no man that would know me: refuge failed me; no man cared for my soul.*

5 *I cried unto thee, O LORD: I said, Thou art my refuge and my portion in the land of the living.*

HEBREWS 13:5–6

5 *Let your conversation be without covetousness; and be content with such things as ye have: for he hath said, I will never leave thee, nor forsake thee.*

6 *So that we may boldly say, The Lord is my helper, and I will not fear what man shall do unto me.*

1 PETER 5:7

7 *Casting all your care upon him; for he careth for you.*

A. He was _____ from Egypt.

ROMANS 8:35–39

35 *Who shall separate us from the love of Christ? shall tribulation, or distress, or persecution, or famine, or nakedness, or peril, or sword?*

36 *As it is written, For thy sake we are killed all the day long; we are accounted as sheep for the slaughter.*

37   Nay, in all these things we are more than conquerors through him that loved us.

38   For I am persuaded, that neither death, nor life, nor angels, nor principalities, nor powers, nor things present, nor things to come,

39   Nor height, nor depth, nor any other creature, shall be able to separate us from the love of God, which is in Christ Jesus our Lord.

B.   He was _____ in the wilderness.

II. Moses Was _____

NUMBERS 12:3

3   (Now the man Moses was very meek, above all the men which were upon the face of the earth.)

JAMES 4:10

10   Humble yourselves in the sight of the Lord, and he shall lift you up.

1 PETER 5:6

6   Humble yourselves therefore under the mighty hand of God, that he may exalt you in due time:

A.   He was no longer a _____.

HEBREWS 11:24–27

24   By faith Moses, when he was come to years, refused to be called the son of Pharaoh's daughter;

25   Choosing rather to suffer affliction with the people of God, than to enjoy the pleasures of sin for a season;

26 Esteeming the reproach of Christ greater riches than the treasures in Egypt: for he had respect unto the recompence of the reward.

27 By faith he forsook Egypt, not fearing the wrath of the king: for he endured, as seeing him who is invisible.

B. He was now a _____.

LUKE 16:10

10 He that is faithful in that which is least is faithful also in much: and he that is unjust in the least is unjust also in much.

MATTHEW 25:21

21 His lord said unto him, Well done, thou good and faithful servant: thou hast been faithful over a few things, I will make thee ruler over many things: enter thou into the joy of thy lord.

1 CORINTHIANS 4:2

2 Moreover it is required in stewards, that a man be found faithful.

III. He Was _____

A. He took time to _____ and _____.

PSALM 39:4–5

4 LORD, make me to know mine end, and the measure of my days, what it is; that I may know how frail I am.

5 Behold, thou hast made my days as an handbreadth; and mine age is as nothing before thee: verily every man at his best state is altogether vanity. Selah.

B. He took time to* _____ *and

_____.

PSALM 90:12

12 So teach us to number our days, that we may apply our hearts unto wisdom.

Conclusion

_____

_____

_____

Study Questions

1. Describe Moses' time in Midian.

2. How did Moses get to be a shepherd in Midian?

3. Why was Moses' time in Midian a humbling experience?

4. What are some thoughts that may have gone through Moses' mind during his time of exile in Midian?

5. How has God worked in your life during times when you felt alone (in terms of human companionship)?

6. Describe a time in your life when you did a good deed and God specially rewarded you for it.

7. Describe an event or events in your life that God used to humble you.

8. What three events in your life would you describe as your most pivotal?

Memory Verse

HEBREWS 11:27
27 By faith he forsook Egypt, not fearing the wrath of the king: for he endured, as seeing him who is invisible.

Moses and the Burning Bush
Listening to the Voice of God

Text

EXODUS 3:1–11

1   Now Moses kept the flock of Jethro his father in law, the priest of Midian: and he led the flock to the backside of the desert, and came to the mountain of God, even to Horeb.

2   And the angel of the LORD appeared unto him in a flame of fire out of the midst of a bush: and he looked, and, behold, the bush burned with fire, and the bush was not consumed.

3   And Moses said, I will now turn aside, and see this great sight, why the bush is not burnt.

4   And when the LORD saw that he turned aside to see, God called unto him out of the midst of the bush, and said, Moses, Moses. And he said, Here am I.

5   And he said, Draw not nigh hither: put off thy shoes from off thy feet, for the place whereon thou standest is holy ground.

6   Moreover he said, I am the God of thy father, the God of Abraham, the God of Isaac, and the God of Jacob. And Moses hid his face; for he was afraid to look upon God.

7   And the LORD said, I have surely seen the affliction of my people which are in Egypt, and have heard their cry by reason of their taskmasters; for I know their sorrows;

8   And I am come down to deliver them out of the hand of the Egyptians, and to bring them up out of that land unto a good land and a large, unto a land flowing with milk and honey; unto the place of the Canaanites, and the Hittites, and the Amorites, and the Perizzites, and the Hivites, and the Jebusites.

9   Now therefore, behold, the cry of the children of Israel is come unto me: and I have also seen the oppression wherewith the Egyptians oppress them.

10   Come now therefore, and I will send thee unto Pharaoh, that thou mayest bring forth my people the children of Israel out of Egypt.

11   And Moses said unto God, Who am I, that I should go unto Pharaoh, and that I should bring forth the children of Israel out of Egypt?

ACTS 7:30–35

30   And when forty years were expired, there appeared to him in the wilderness of mount Sina an angel of the Lord in a flame of fire in a bush.

31   When Moses saw it, he wondered at the sight: and as he drew near to behold it, the voice of the Lord came unto him,

32   Saying, I am the God of thy fathers, the God of Abraham, and the God of Isaac, and the God of Jacob. Then Moses trembled, and durst not behold.

33   Then said the Lord to him, Put off thy shoes from thy feet: for the place where thou standest is holy ground.

34   I have seen, I have seen the affliction of my people which is in Egypt, and I have heard their groaning, and am come down to deliver them. And now come, I will send thee into Egypt.

35   This Moses whom they refused, saying, Who made thee a ruler and a judge? the same did God send to be a ruler and a deliverer by the hand of the angel which appeared to him in the bush.

Overview

God has a definite purpose and a detailed plan for each of our lives. We may feel incapable of doing what God wants us to do; indeed, in our own strength and wisdom we cannot fulfill God's will. But God will not send us where He cannot sustain us, and He will fully equip us for His service. Our part is to surrender and obey.

Introduction

_____

_____

_____

I. Moses Gave His _____ (Exodus 3:1–4; Acts 7:30–31)

1 CORINTHIANS 4:2

2   Moreover it is required in stewards, that a man be found faithful.

LUKE 9:51

51   And it came to pass, when the time was come that he should be received up, he stedfastly set his face to go to Jerusalem.

A. *The bush was* _____ *(Exodus 3:1–4; Acts 7:30–31).*

B. *The bush was not* _____ *(Exodus 3:2).*

HEBREWS 4:14–16

14   Seeing then that we have a great high priest, that is passed into the heavens, Jesus the Son of God, let us hold fast our profession.

15   For we have not an high priest which cannot be touched with the feeling of our infirmities; but was in all points tempted like as we are, yet without sin.

16   Let us therefore come boldly unto the throne of grace, that we may obtain mercy, and find grace to help in time of need.

II. Moses Gave His _____
(Exodus 3:5–6; Acts 7:32–33)

A. *He was on _____ ground (Exodus 3:5; Acts 7:32–33).*

HEBREWS 9:11–14

11 But Christ being come an high priest of good things to come, by a greater and more perfect tabernacle, not made with hands, that is to say, not of this building;

12 Neither by the blood of goats and calves, but by his own blood he entered in once into the holy place, having obtained eternal redemption for us.

13 For if the blood of bulls and of goats, and the ashes of an heifer sprinkling the unclean, sanctifieth to the purifying of the flesh:

14 How much more shall the blood of Christ, who through the eternal Spirit offered himself without spot to God, purge your conscience from dead works to serve the living God?

PHILIPPIANS 3:4–6

4 Though I might also have confidence in the flesh. If any other man thinketh that he hath whereof he might trust in the flesh, I more:

5 Circumcised the eighth day, of the stock of Israel, of the tribe of Benjamin, an Hebrew of the Hebrews; as touching the law, a Pharisee;

6 Concerning zeal, persecuting the church; touching the righteousness which is in the law, blameless.

ACTS 22:3–4

3 I am verily a man which am a Jew, born in Tarsus, a city in Cilicia, yet brought up in this city at the feet of Gamaliel, and taught according to the perfect manner of

the law of the fathers, and was zealous toward God, as ye all are this day.

4 *And I persecuted this way unto the death, binding and delivering into prisons both men and women.*

B. He had a _____ response (Exodus 3:6; Acts 7:32).

2 CHRONICLES 7:14

14 *If my people, which are called by my name, shall humble themselves, and pray, and seek my face, and turn from their wicked ways; then will I hear from heaven, and will forgive their sin, and will heal their land.*

PROVERBS 3:34

34 *Surely he scorneth the scorners: but he giveth grace unto the lowly.*

JAMES 4:6, 10

6 *But he giveth more grace. Wherefore he saith, God resisteth the proud, but giveth grace unto the humble.*

10 *Humble yourselves in the sight of the Lord, and he shall lift you up.*

1 PETER 5:5–6

5 *Likewise, ye younger, submit yourselves unto the elder. Yea, all of you be subject one to another, and be clothed with humility: for God resisteth the proud, and giveth grace to the humble.*

6 *Humble yourselves therefore under the mighty hand of God, that he may exalt you in due time:*

III. Moses Gave His _____
(Exodus 3:7–4:31; Acts 7:34–35)

A. *He made* _____ *(Exodus 3:7–4:17).*

B. *He made* _____ *(Exodus 4:18–23;*
   Acts 7:34–35).

   1. There was a change in Moses' country.

   2. There was a change in Moses' calling.

Conclusion

_____

_____

_____

Study Questions

1. What did God use to get Moses' attention as he watched the sheep in the wilderness?

2. What did God demand of Moses as he came into His presence at the burning bush?

3. What did God command Moses to do?

4. What excuses did Moses give to God?

5. What are some incidents God has used in your life when He wanted to get your attention?

6.   How can we show reverence to God?

7.   What excuses are you tempted to make that will hold you back from God's service?

8.   What changes might you need to make in your life in obedience to God?

Memory Verses

EXODUS 3:4–5

4   *And when the LORD saw that he turned aside to see, God called unto him out of the midst of the bush, and said, Moses, Moses. And he said, Here am I.*

5   *And he said, Draw not nigh hither: put off thy shoes from off thy feet, for the place whereon thou standest is holy ground.*

LESSON FOUR

Moses and Pharaoh
Living with Difficult People

Text

EXODUS 5:1–9

1   *And afterward Moses and Aaron went in, and told Pharaoh, Thus saith the LORD God of Israel, Let my people go, that they may hold a feast unto me in the wilderness.*

2   *And Pharaoh said, Who is the LORD, that I should obey his voice to let Israel go? I know not the LORD, neither will I let Israel go.*

3   *And they said, The God of the Hebrews hath met with us: let us go, we pray thee, three days' journey into the desert, and sacrifice unto the LORD our God; lest he fall upon us with pestilence, or with the sword.*

4   *And the king of Egypt said unto them, Wherefore do ye, Moses and Aaron, let the people from their works? get you unto your burdens.*

5   *And Pharaoh said, Behold, the people of the land now are many, and ye make them rest from their burdens.*

6   *And Pharaoh commanded the same day the taskmasters of the people, and their officers, saying,*

7   *Ye shall no more give the people straw to make brick, as heretofore: let them go and gather straw for themselves.*

8   *And the tale of the bricks, which they did make heretofore, ye shall lay upon them; ye shall not diminish ought thereof: for they be idle; therefore they cry, saying, Let us go and sacrifice to our God.*

9   *Let there more work be laid upon the men, that they may labour therein; and let them not regard vain words.*

Overview

God is reasonable and patient, but He will not be scorned. The heathen may rage (Psalm 2), but God is sovereign. Those who defy Him will be judged and judged severely, but God will show Himself faithful to those who are faithful to Him.

Introduction

_____

_____

_____

I. The Appeal of _____

2 CORINTHIANS 5:20
20 *Now then we are ambassadors for Christ, as though God did beseech you by us: we pray you in Christ's stead, be ye reconciled to God.*

ACTS 5:32
32 *And we are his witnesses of these things; and so is also the Holy Ghost, whom God hath given to them that obey him.*

A. *He spoke for _____.*

EXODUS 6:10–11, 28–29
10 *And the LORD spake unto Moses, saying,*
11 *Go in, speak unto Pharaoh king of Egypt, that he let the children of Israel go out of his land.*
28 *And it came to pass on the day when the LORD spake unto Moses in the land of Egypt,*
29 *That the LORD spake unto Moses, saying, I am the LORD: speak thou unto Pharaoh king of Egypt all that I say unto thee.*

PSALM 119:130
130 *The entrance of thy words giveth light; it giveth understanding unto the simple.*

Isaiah 55:11

11 *So shall my word be that goeth forth out of my mouth: it shall not return unto me void, but it shall accomplish that which I please, and it shall prosper in the thing whereto I sent it.*

Hebrews 4:12

12 *For the word of God is quick, and powerful, and sharper than any twoedged sword, piercing even to the dividing asunder of soul and spirit, and of the joints and marrow, and is a discerner of the thoughts and intents of the heart.*

2 Timothy 1:13

13 *Hold fast the form of sound words, which thou hast heard of me, in faith and love which is in Christ Jesus.*

B. He spoke for God's _____.

1 Thessalonians 5:14

14 *Now we exhort you, brethren, warn them that are unruly, comfort the feebleminded, support the weak, be patient toward all men.*

Proverbs 14:31

31 *He that oppresseth the poor reproacheth his Maker: but he that honoureth him hath mercy on the poor.*

II. The Arrogance of _____

Psalm 2:1–5

1 *Why do the heathen rage, and the people imagine a vain thing?*

2   *The kings of the earth set themselves, and the rulers take counsel together, against the* LORD, *and against his anointed, saying,*

3   *Let us break their bands asunder, and cast away their cords from us.*

4   *He that sitteth in the heavens shall laugh: the Lord shall have them in derision.*

5   *Then shall he speak unto them in his wrath, and vex them in his sore displeasure.*

A. **He was motivated by _____.**

1. **What Pride Is**

2. **What Pride Is Not**

EXODUS 7:22–23

22   *And the magicians of Egypt did so with their enchantments: and Pharaoh's heart was hardened, neither did he hearken unto them; as the* LORD *had said.*

23   *And Pharaoh turned and went into his house, neither did he set his heart to this also.*

ISAIAH 14:13–14

13   *...I will ascend into heaven, I will exalt my throne above the stars of God: I will sit also upon the mount of the congregation, in the sides of the north:*

14   *I will ascend above the heights of the clouds; I will be like the most High.*

B. **He was motivated by _____.**

EXODUS 8:25–32

25 And Pharaoh called for Moses and for Aaron, and said, Go ye, sacrifice to your God in the land.

26 And Moses said, It is not meet so to do; for we shall sacrifice the abomination of the Egyptians to the LORD our God: lo, shall we sacrifice the abomination of the Egyptians before their eyes, and will they not stone us?

27 We will go three days' journey into the wilderness, and sacrifice to the LORD our God, as he shall command us.

28 And Pharaoh said, I will let you go, that ye may sacrifice to the LORD your God in the wilderness; only ye shall not go very far away: intreat for me.

29 And Moses said, Behold, I go out from thee, and I will intreat the LORD that the swarms of flies may depart from Pharaoh, from his servants, and from his people, to morrow: but let not Pharaoh deal deceitfully any more in not letting the people go to sacrifice to the LORD.

30 And Moses went out from Pharaoh, and intreated the LORD.

31 And the LORD did according to the word of Moses; and he removed the swarms of flies from Pharaoh, from his servants, and from his people; there remained not one.

32 And Pharaoh hardened his heart at this time also, neither would he let the people go.

III. The Anger of _____

A. Judgment was _____.

EXODUS 11:1–10

1 And the LORD said unto Moses, Yet will I bring one plague more upon Pharaoh, and upon Egypt; afterwards he will let you go hence: when he shall let you go, he shall surely thrust you out hence altogether.

2   *Speak now in the ears of the people, and let every man borrow of his neighbour, and every woman of her neighbour, jewels of silver, and jewels of gold.*

3   *And the* LORD *gave the people favour in the sight of the Egyptians. Moreover the man Moses was very great in the land of Egypt, in the sight of Pharaoh's servants, and in the sight of the people.*

4   *And Moses said, Thus saith the* LORD, *About midnight will I go out into the midst of Egypt:*

5   *And all the firstborn in the land of Egypt shall die, from the firstborn of Pharaoh that sitteth upon his throne, even unto the firstborn of the maidservant that is behind the mill; and all the firstborn of beasts.*

6   *And there shall be a great cry throughout all the land of Egypt, such as there was none like it, nor shall be like it any more.*

7   *But against any of the children of Israel shall not a dog move his tongue, against man or beast: that ye may know how that the* LORD *doth put a difference between the Egyptians and Israel.*

8   *And all these thy servants shall come down unto me, and bow down themselves unto me, saying, Get thee out, and all the people that follow thee: and after that I will go out. And he went out from Pharaoh in a great anger.*

9   *And the* LORD *said unto Moses, Pharaoh shall not hearken unto you; that my wonders may be multiplied in the land of Egypt.*

10   *And Moses and Aaron did all these wonders before Pharaoh: and the* LORD *hardened Pharaoh's heart, so that he would not let the children of Israel go out of his land.*

1. **Salvation was scorned (Exodus 11:9–10).**

2. **Salvation was accepted (Exodus 12:21–28).**

EXODUS 12:21–28

21 Then Moses called for all the elders of Israel, and said unto them, Draw out and take you a lamb according to your families, and kill the passover.

22 And ye shall take a bunch of hyssop, and dip it in the blood that is in the bason, and strike the lintel and the two side posts with the blood that is in the bason; and none of you shall go out at the door of his house until the morning.

23 For the LORD will pass through to smite the Egyptians; and when he seeth the blood upon the lintel, and on the two side posts, the LORD will pass over the door, and will not suffer the destroyer to come in unto your houses to smite you.

24 And ye shall observe this thing for an ordinance to thee and to thy sons for ever.

25 And it shall come to pass, when ye be come to the land which the LORD will give you, according as he hath promised, that ye shall keep this service.

26 And it shall come to pass, when your children shall say unto you, What mean ye by this service?

27 That ye shall say, It is the sacrifice of the LORD's passover, who passed over the houses of the children of Israel in Egypt, when he smote the Egyptians, and delivered our houses. And the people bowed the head and worshipped.

28 And the children of Israel went away, and did as the LORD had commanded Moses and Aaron, so did they.

B. Judgment was _____.

EXODUS 12:29–36

29 And it came to pass, that at midnight the LORD smote all the firstborn in the land of Egypt, from the firstborn of Pharaoh that sat on his throne unto the firstborn of

the captive that was in the dungeon; and all the firstborn of cattle.

30 And Pharaoh rose up in the night, he, and all his servants, and all the Egyptians; and there was a great cry in Egypt; for there was not a house where there was not one dead.

31 And he called for Moses and Aaron by night, and said, Rise up, and get you forth from among my people, both ye and the children of Israel; and go, serve the LORD, as ye have said.

32 Also take your flocks and your herds, as ye have said, and be gone; and bless me also.

33 And the Egyptians were urgent upon the people, that they might send them out of the land in haste; for they said, We be all dead men.

34 And the people took their dough before it was leavened, their kneadingtroughs being bound up in their clothes upon their shoulders.

35 And the children of Israel did according to the word of Moses; and they borrowed of the Egyptians jewels of silver, and jewels of gold, and raiment:

36 And the LORD gave the people favour in the sight of the Egyptians, so that they lent unto them such things as they required. And they spoiled the Egyptians.

Conclusion

_____

_____

_____

Study Questions

1. What was the message Moses carried to Pharaoh on God's behalf?

2. What was Pharaoh's response to the appeal of Moses?

3. List some of the plagues God brought upon Egypt.

4. What did the Israelites have to do in order to avoid the death of their firstborn?

5. What opportunities do you have to speak for God in the course of your daily life?

6. What opportunities do you have to stand up for others in the course of your daily life?

7. In what ways do we see the arrogance of the world displayed today?

8. What does the Bible say about God's coming judgment on this world?

Memory Verse

PROVERBS 14:31

31 He that oppresseth the poor reproacheth his Maker: but he that honoureth him hath mercy on the poor.

Moses and the Red Sea
Trusting God in Difficult Times

Text

EXODUS 14:19–31

19 And the angel of God, which went before the camp of Israel, removed and went behind them; and the pillar of the cloud went from before their face, and stood behind them:

20 And it came between the camp of the Egyptians and the camp of Israel; and it was a cloud and darkness to them, but it gave light by night to these: so that the one came not near the other all the night.

21 And Moses stretched out his hand over the sea; and the LORD caused the sea to go back by a strong east wind all that night, and made the sea dry land, and the waters were divided.

22 And the children of Israel went into the midst of the sea upon the dry ground: and the waters were a wall unto them on their right hand, and on their left.

23 And the Egyptians pursued, and went in after them to the midst of the sea, even all Pharaoh's horses, his chariots, and his horsemen.

24 And it came to pass, that in the morning watch the LORD looked unto the host of the Egyptians through the pillar of fire and of the cloud, and troubled the host of the Egyptians,

25 And took off their chariot wheels, that they drave them heavily: so that the Egyptians said, Let us flee from the face of Israel; for the LORD fighteth for them against the Egyptians.

26 And the LORD said unto Moses, Stretch out thine hand over the sea, that the waters may come again upon the Egyptians, upon their chariots, and upon their horsemen.

27 And Moses stretched forth his hand over the sea, and the sea returned to his strength when the morning appeared; and the Egyptians fled against it; and the LORD *overthrew the Egyptians in the midst of the sea.*

28 And the waters returned, and covered the chariots, and the horsemen, and all the host of Pharaoh that came into the sea after them; there remained not so much as one of them.

29 But the children of Israel walked upon dry land in the midst of the sea; and the waters were a wall unto them on their right hand, and on their left.

30 Thus the LORD *saved Israel that day out of the hand of the Egyptians; and Israel saw the Egyptians dead upon the sea shore.*

31 And Israel saw that great work which the LORD *did upon the Egyptians: and the people feared the* LORD, *and believed the* LORD, *and his servant Moses.*

Overview

God's people see circumstances differently than the world sees them. A submissive and obedient relationship with God makes all the difference. God works in miraculous ways as His people obey His directions. His people should rejoice in His mercy and His mighty works.

Introduction

_____

_____

_____

I. The _____ (vv. 19–20)

A. God's people saw _____ (vv. 19–20).

EXODUS 13:21–22

21 And the LORD went before them by day in a pillar of a cloud, to lead them the way; and by night in a pillar of fire, to give them light; to go by day and night:

22 He took not away the pillar of the cloud by day, nor the pillar of fire by night, from before the people.

JOHN 8:12

12 ...I am the light of the world: he that followeth me shall not walk in darkness, but shall have the light of life.

B. God's enemies saw _____ (v. 20).

II. The _____ (vv. 21–31)

A. God's people had _____ (vv. 21–22, 29–31).

PSALM 23:4

4 Yea, though I walk through the valley of the shadow of death, I will fear no evil: for thou art with me....

B. God's enemies had _____ (vv. 23–28).

III. The _____ (vv. 28, 31)

HEBREWS 13:15

15 By him therefore let us offer the sacrifice of praise to God continually, that is, the fruit of our lips giving thanks to his name.

EPHESIANS 5:19

19 Speaking to yourselves in psalms and hymns and spiritual songs, singing and making melody in your heart to the Lord;

COLOSSIANS 3:16

16 Let the word of Christ dwell in you richly in all wisdom; teaching and admonishing one another in psalms and hymns and spiritual songs, singing with grace in your hearts to the Lord.

A. *God's people _____ (v. 31).*

ECCLESIASTES 12:13

13 Let us hear the conclusion of the whole matter: Fear God, and keep his commandments: for this is the whole duty of man.

DEUTERONOMY 8:11, 18

11 Beware that thou forget not the LORD thy God, in not keeping his commandments, and his judgments, and his statutes, which I command thee this day:

18 But thou shalt remember the LORD thy God: for it is he that giveth thee power to get wealth, that he may establish his covenant which he sware unto thy fathers, as it is this day.

1 THESSALONIANS 5:18

18 In every thing give thanks: for this is the will of God in Christ Jesus concerning you.

HEBREWS 13:5

5   *Let your conversation be without covetousness; and be content with such things as ye have: for he hath said, I will never leave thee, nor forsake thee.*

B.   God's enemies _____ **(v. 28).**

EXODUS 12:30

30 And Pharaoh rose up in the night, he, and all his servants, and all the Egyptians; and there was a great cry in Egypt; for there was not a house where there was not one dead.

EXODUS 14:28

28 And the waters returned, and covered the chariots, and the horsemen, and all the host of Pharaoh that came into the sea after them; there remained not so much as one of them.

ROMANS 11:29

29 For the gifts and calling of God are without repentance.

Conclusion

_____

_____

_____

Study Questions

1. What did God use to lead His people as they left Egypt?

2. What did the Egyptian army see as they approached the Israelites by the edge of the Red Sea?

3. Describe how God made a way for His people through the Red Sea.

4. Describe what happened to the Egyptian army as they pursued the Israelites.

5. How does God lead us today?

6. What are some miracles you believe God has performed on your behalf or on the behalf of people you know?

7. What can we do to become Christians who consistently rejoice?

8. According to Ecclesiastes, what is our whole duty in life?

Memory Verse

1 THESSALONIANS 5:18
18 In every thing give thanks: for this is the will of God in Christ Jesus concerning you.

Moses and the Manna
Learning the Power of Contentment

Text

EXODUS 16:1–23

1 And they took their journey from Elim, and all the congregation of the children of Israel came unto the wilderness of Sin, which is between Elim and Sinai, on the fifteenth day of the second month after their departing out of the land of Egypt.

2 And the whole congregation of the children of Israel murmured against Moses and Aaron in the wilderness:

3 And the children of Israel said unto them, Would to God we had died by the hand of the LORD in the land of Egypt, when we sat by the flesh pots, and when we did eat bread to the full; for ye have brought us forth into this wilderness, to kill this whole assembly with hunger.

4 Then said the LORD unto Moses, Behold, I will rain bread from heaven for you; and the people shall go out and gather a certain rate every day, that I may prove them, whether they will walk in my law, or no.

5 And it shall come to pass, that on the sixth day they shall prepare that which they bring in; and it shall be twice as much as they gather daily.

6 And Moses and Aaron said unto all the children of Israel, At even, then ye shall know that the LORD hath brought you out from the land of Egypt:

7 And in the morning, then ye shall see the glory of the LORD; for that he heareth your murmurings against the LORD: and what are we, that ye murmur against us?

8   And Moses said, This shall be, when the LORD shall give
you in the evening flesh to eat, and in the morning bread to
the full; for that the LORD heareth your murmurings which
ye murmur against him: and what are we? your murmurings
are not against us, but against the LORD.

9   And Moses spake unto Aaron, Say unto all the congregation
of the children of Israel, Come near before the LORD: for he
hath heard your murmurings.

10   And it came to pass, as Aaron spake unto the whole
congregation of the children of Israel, that they looked toward
the wilderness, and, behold, the glory of the LORD appeared in
the cloud.

11   And the LORD spake unto Moses, saying,

12   I have heard the murmurings of the children of Israel:
speak unto them, saying, At even ye shall eat flesh, and in the
morning ye shall be filled with bread; and ye shall know that
I am the LORD your God.

13   And it came to pass, that at even the quails came up, and
covered the camp: and in the morning the dew lay round
about the host.

14   And when the dew that lay was gone up, behold, upon the
face of the wilderness there lay a small round thing, as small
as the hoar frost on the ground.

15   And when the children of Israel saw it, they said one to
another, It is manna: for they wist not what it was. And Moses
said unto them, This is the bread which the LORD hath given
you to eat.

16   This is the thing which the LORD hath commanded, Gather
of it every man according to his eating, an omer for every man,
according to the number of your persons; take ye every man
for them which are in his tents.

17   And the children of Israel did so, and gathered, some more,
some less.

18   And when they did mete it with an omer, he that gathered much had nothing over, and he that gathered little had no lack; they gathered every man according to his eating.

19   And Moses said, Let no man leave of it till the morning.

20   Notwithstanding they hearkened not unto Moses; but some of them left of it until the morning, and it bred worms, and stank: and Moses was wroth with them.

21   And they gathered it every morning, every man according to his eating: and when the sun waxed hot, it melted.

22   And it came to pass, that on the sixth day they gathered twice as much bread, two omers for one man: and all the rulers of the congregation came and told Moses.

23   And he said unto them, This is that which the L<small>ORD</small> hath said, To morrow is the rest of the holy sabbath unto the L<small>ORD</small>: bake that which ye will bake to day, and seethe that ye will seethe; and that which remaineth over lay up for you to be kept until the morning.

Overview

"Where God guides, God provides" is a saying spoken repeatedly but is rarely more perfectly illustrated than in this account of the miraculous provision of food sufficient for so many people in a barren wilderness. We, too, can be assured that God will meet our needs as we follow His leading in our lives.

Introduction

_____

_____

_____

I. The _____ (vv. 2–3, 8)

MATTHEW 10:29–31

29 Are not two sparrows sold for a farthing? and one of them shall not fall on the ground without your Father.

30 But the very hairs of your head are all numbered.

31 Fear ye not therefore, ye are of more value than many sparrows.

ISAIAH 55:8–9

8 For my thoughts are not your thoughts, neither are your ways my ways, saith the LORD.

9 For as the heavens are higher than the earth, so are my ways higher than your ways, and my thoughts than your thoughts.

 A. *The people were _____ (vv. 2–3).*

  1. **The people complained.**

  2. **The people forgot.**

  1 CORINTHIANS 15:31

  31 ...I die daily.

  MARK 8:34–35

  34 ...Whosoever will come after me, let him deny himself, and take up his cross, and follow me.

  35 For whosoever will save his life shall lose it; but whosoever shall lose his life for my sake and the gospel's, the same shall save it.

B. The people made _____ **(v. 8).**

1 THESSALONIANS 5:16–18

16 *Rejoice evermore.*

17 *Pray without ceasing.*

18 *In every thing give thanks: for this is the will of God in Christ Jesus concerning you.*

II. The _____ (vv. 4–10)

A. They saw God's _____ **(vv. 4–5).**

EPHESIANS 4:31–32

31 *Let all bitterness, and wrath, and anger, and clamour, and evil speaking, be put away from you, with all malice:*

32 *And be ye kind one to another, tenderhearted, forgiving one another, even as God for Christ's sake hath forgiven you.*

B. They saw God's _____ **(vv. 6–10).**

III. The _____

1 THESSALONIANS 4:1

1 *Furthermore then we beseech you, brethren, and exhort you by the Lord Jesus, that as ye have received of us how ye ought to walk and to please God, so ye would abound more and more.*

1 CORINTHIANS 10:31

31 *Whether therefore ye eat, or drink, or whatsoever ye do, do all to the glory of God.*

HEBREWS 11:6

6   But without faith it is impossible to please him: for he that cometh to God must believe that he is, and that he is a rewarder of them that diligently seek him.

A.   God gave _____ (vv. 11–23).

1.   Gather enough for each person.

ROMANS 8:32

32   He that spared not his own Son, but delivered him up for us all, how shall he not with him also freely give us all things?

2.   Gather enough for each day.

LAMENTATIONS 3:22–23

22   It is of the LORD's mercies that we are not consumed, because his compassions fail not.
23   They are new every morning: great is thy faithfulness.

3.   Gather extra for the Sabbath.

EXODUS 16:25–27

25   And Moses said, Eat that to day; for to day is a sabbath unto the LORD: to day ye shall not find it in the field.
26   Six days ye shall gather it; but on the seventh day, which is the sabbath, in it there shall be none.
27   And it came to pass, that there went out some of the people on the seventh day for to gather, and they found none.

PROVERBS 3:5–8

5   *Trust in the LORD with all thine heart; and lean not unto thine own understanding.*

6   *In all thy ways acknowledge him, and he shall direct thy paths.*

7   *Be not wise in thine own eyes: fear the LORD, and depart from evil.*

8   *It shall be health to thy navel, and marrow to thy bones.*

B. God gave _____ *(v. 23).*

EXODUS 16:31, 35

31 *And the house of Israel called the name thereof Manna: and it was like coriander seed, white; and the taste of it was like wafers made with honey.*

35 *And the children of Israel did eat manna forty years, until they came to a land inhabited; they did eat manna, until they came unto the borders of the land of Canaan.*

Conclusion

_____

_____

_____

Study Questions

1. What is meant by the Bible term *murmuring*?

2. Why was the people's murmuring such a serious matter?

3. How can we keep from having a spirit of murmuring?

4. Describe the manna that God provided for His people.

5. What were some of the rules God set down for what the people were to do with the manna?

6. Tell about a time in your life when God provided for you in an unexpected way.

7. In what ways have you seen the glory of God?

8. Tell about a time when you obeyed God in faith and saw Him do something miraculous in response.

Memory Verses

MATTHEW 6:31–33

31 Therefore take no thought, saying, What shall we eat? or, What shall we drink? or, Wherewithal shall we be clothed?
32 (For after all these things do the Gentiles seek:) for your heavenly Father knoweth that ye have need of all these things.
33 But seek ye first the kingdom of God, and his righteousness; and all these things shall be added unto you.

Moses and His Faithful Friends
Following the Faith of God's Leader

Text

EXODUS 17:8–13

8 Then came Amalek, and fought with Israel in Rephidim.

9 And Moses said unto Joshua, Choose us out men, and go out, fight with Amalek: to morrow I will stand on the top of the hill with the rod of God in mine hand.

10 So Joshua did as Moses had said to him, and fought with Amalek: and Moses, Aaron, and Hur went up to the top of the hill.

11 And it came to pass, when Moses held up his hand, that Israel prevailed: and when he let down his hand, Amalek prevailed.

12 But Moses' hands were heavy; and they took a stone, and put it under him, and he sat thereon; and Aaron and Hur stayed up his hands, the one on the one side, and the other on the other side; and his hands were steady until the going down of the sun.

13 And Joshua discomfited Amalek and his people with the edge of the sword.

Overview

God's leaders who are serving from a pure heart and biblical foundation need the fellowship and support of their followers. When God's people work together and pray for God's blessing, God can and will do mighty works on their behalf.

Introduction

_____

_____

_____

I. The _____ of Moses' Faith (vv. 8–11)

A. The army was _____ (vv. 8–9).

EPHESIANS 6:10–18

10 *Finally, my brethren, be strong in the Lord, and in the power of his might.*

11 *Put on the whole armour of God, that ye may be able to stand against the wiles of the devil.*

12 *For we wrestle not against flesh and blood, but against principalities, against powers, against the rulers of the darkness of this world, against spiritual wickedness in high places.*

13 *Wherefore take unto you the whole armour of God, that ye may be able to withstand in the evil day, and having done all, to stand.*

14 *Stand therefore, having your loins girt about with truth, and having on the breastplate of righteousness;*

15 *And your feet shod with the preparation of the gospel of peace;*

16 *Above all, taking the shield of faith, wherewith ye shall be able to quench all the fiery darts of the wicked.*

17 *And take the helmet of salvation, and the sword of the Spirit, which is the word of God:*

18   *Praying always with all prayer and supplication in the Spirit, and watching thereunto with all perseverance and supplication for all saints;*

2 Timothy 2:3–4

3   *Thou therefore endure hardness, as a good soldier of Jesus Christ.*

4   *No man that warreth entangleth himself with the affairs of this life; that he may please him who hath chosen him to be a soldier.*

B.   God showed His _____ (vv. 9–11).

Zechariah 4:6

6   *…Not by might, nor by power, but by my spirit, saith the Lord of hosts.*

II. The _____ of Moses' Hands (v. 11)

A.   When his hands were up, _____ prevailed (v. 11a).

Matthew 11:28–30

28   *Come unto me, all ye that labour and are heavy laden, and I will give you rest.*

29   *Take my yoke upon you, and learn of me; for I am meek and lowly in heart: and ye shall find rest unto your souls.*

30   *For my yoke is easy, and my burden is light.*

B.   When his hands were down, _____ prevailed (v. 11b).

Isaiah 40:28–31

28 Hast thou not known? hast thou not heard, that the everlasting God, the Lord, the Creator of the ends of the earth, fainteth not, neither is weary? there is no searching of his understanding.

29 He giveth power to the faint; and to them that have no might he increaseth strength.

30 Even the youths shall faint and be weary, and the young men shall utterly fall:

31 But they that wait upon the Lord shall renew their strength; they shall mount up with wings as eagles; they shall run, and not be weary; and they shall walk, and not faint.

III. The _____ of Moses' Friends (vv. 10–13)

A. They set out for the _____ (v. 10).

B. They set out a _____ (v. 12).

1 Thessalonians 5:12–13

12 And we beseech you, brethren, to know them which labour among you, and are over you in the Lord, and admonish you;

13 And to esteem them very highly in love for their work's sake. And be at peace among yourselves.

Hebrews 13:7, 17

7 Remember them which have the rule over you, who have spoken unto you the word of God: whose faith follow, considering the end of their conversation.

17 Obey them that have the rule over you, and submit yourselves: for they watch for your souls, as they that must give account, that they may do it with joy, and not with grief: for that is unprofitable for you.

C. They stayed up his _____ (v. 12).

1 CORINTHIANS 12:18, 27–28

18 But now hath God set the members every one of them in the body, as it hath pleased him.

27 Now ye are the body of Christ, and members in particular.

28 And God hath set some in the church, first apostles, secondarily prophets, thirdly teachers, after that miracles, then gifts of healings, helps, governments, diversities of tongues.

D. They stayed until the battle was _____ (vv. 12–13).

Conclusion

_____

_____

_____

Study Questions

1. What was Moses' role in the battle with the Amalekites?

2. Who went with Moses to the top of the hill?

3. How did the position of Moses' hands determine the course of the battle?

4. How did Aaron and Hur contribute to the victory of Israel over Amalek?

5. Tell about an incident in your life when you knew beyond a doubt that God was empowering you.

6. Describe a time in your life when you were discouraged and you found encouragement in the Word of God. What verse or verses helped you during this time?

7. Tell about a time when a friend or friends supported you and what the support meant to you.

8. What are some things we can do to help support our spiritual leaders?

Memory Verse

1 CORINTHIANS 12:18

18 But now hath God set the members every one of them in the body, as it hath pleased him.

Moses on the Mountain
Obeying God's Commands

Text

EXODUS 20:1–18

1 And God spake all these words, saying,

2 I am the LORD thy God, which have brought thee out of the land of Egypt, out of the house of bondage.

3 Thou shalt have no other gods before me.

4 Thou shalt not make unto thee any graven image, or any likeness of any thing that is in heaven above, or that is in the earth beneath, or that is in the water under the earth:

5 Thou shalt not bow down thyself to them, nor serve them: for I the LORD thy God am a jealous God, visiting the iniquity of the fathers upon the children unto the third and fourth generation of them that hate me;

6 And shewing mercy unto thousands of them that love me, and keep my commandments.

7 Thou shalt not take the name of the LORD thy God in vain; for the LORD will not hold him guiltless that taketh his name in vain.

8 Remember the sabbath day, to keep it holy.

9 Six days shalt thou labour, and do all thy work:

10 But the seventh day is the sabbath of the LORD thy God: in it thou shalt not do any work, thou, nor thy son, nor thy daughter, thy manservant, nor thy maidservant, nor thy cattle, nor thy stranger that is within thy gates:

11 For in six days the LORD made heaven and earth, the sea, and all that in them is, and rested the seventh day: wherefore the LORD blessed the sabbath day, and hallowed it.

12   *Honour thy father and thy mother: that thy days may be long upon the land which the* LORD *thy God giveth thee.*

13   *Thou shalt not kill.*

14   *Thou shalt not commit adultery.*

15   *Thou shalt not steal.*

16   *Thou shalt not bear false witness against thy neighbour.*

17   *Thou shalt not covet thy neighbour's house, thou shalt not covet thy neighbour's wife, nor his manservant, nor his maidservant, nor his ox, nor his ass, nor any thing that is thy neighbour's.*

18   *And all the people saw the thunderings, and the lightnings, and the noise of the trumpet, and the mountain smoking: and when the people saw it, they removed, and stood afar off.*

Overview

God is not a selfish dictator. He knows what is best for us and does everything He can to guide us in the right ways. He has abundantly proven His love, and we should respond to that love with trust and obedience.

Introduction

_____

_____

_____

I. The _____ Commitments

A. _____ *made a pledge to the people.*

EXODUS 19:3–6

3   And Moses went up unto God, and the LORD called
unto him out of the mountain, saying, Thus shalt thou
say to the house of Jacob, and tell the children of Israel;

4   Ye have seen what I did unto the Egyptians, and how
I bare you on eagles' wings, and brought you unto myself.

5   Now therefore, if ye will obey my voice indeed, and
keep my covenant, then ye shall be a peculiar treasure
unto me above all people: for all the earth is mine:

6   And ye shall be unto me a kingdom of priests, and an
holy nation. These are the words which thou shalt speak
unto the children of Israel.

LEVITICUS 19:2

2   Speak unto all the congregation of the children of
Israel, and say unto them, Ye shall be holy: for I the LORD
your God am holy.

LEVITICUS 20:26

26 And ye shall be holy unto me: for I the LORD am holy,
and have severed you from other people, that ye should
be mine.

1 Peter 1:15–16

15　But as he which hath called you is holy, so be ye holy in all manner of conversation;

16　Because it is written, Be ye holy; for I am holy.

1 Corinthians 2:9

9　But as it is written, Eye hath not seen, nor ear heard, neither have entered into the heart of man, the things which God hath prepared for them that love him.

John 14:21

21　He that hath my commandments, and keepeth them, he it is that loveth me: and he that loveth me shall be loved of my Father, and I will love him, and will manifest myself to him.

B.　The _____ made a pledge to God.

Exodus 19:8

8　And all the people answered together, and said, All that the Lord hath spoken we will do. And Moses returned the words of the people unto the Lord.

James 2:10–11

10　For whosoever shall keep the whole law, and yet offend in one point, he is guilty of all.

11　For he that said, Do not commit adultery, said also, Do not kill. Now if thou commit no adultery, yet if thou kill, thou art become a transgressor of the law.

II. The _____ Commandments

A.　They listed man's duties to _____.

ISAIAH 45:18

18 For thus saith the LORD that created the heavens; God himself that formed the earth and made it; he hath established it, he created it not in vain, he formed it to be inhabited: I am the LORD; and there is none else.

2 CHRONICLES 36:14–16

14 Moreover all the chief of the priests, and the people, transgressed very much after all the abominations of the heathen; and polluted the house of the LORD which he had hallowed in Jerusalem.

15 And the LORD God of their fathers sent to them by his messengers, rising up betimes, and sending; because he had compassion on his people, and on his dwelling place:

16 But they mocked the messengers of God, and despised his words, and misused his prophets, until the wrath of the LORD arose against his people, till there was no remedy.

ROMANS 13:7

7 Render therefore to all their dues: tribute to whom tribute is due; custom to whom custom; fear to whom fear; honour to whom honour.

LEVITICUS 24:16

16 And he that blasphemeth the name of the LORD, he shall surely be put to death....

HEBREWS 10:25

25 Not forsaking the assembling of ourselves together, as the manner of some is; but exhorting one another: and so much the more, as ye see the day approaching.

B. They listed man's duties to other _____.

Ephesians 6:1–2

1   Children, obey your parents in the Lord: for this is right.
2   Honour thy father and mother; (which is the first commandment with promise;)

Colossians 3:20

20   Children, obey your parents in all things: for this is well pleasing unto the Lord.

2 Timothy 3:1–5

1   This know also, that in the last days perilous times shall come.
2   For men shall be lovers of their own selves, covetous, boasters, proud, blasphemers, disobedient to parents, unthankful, unholy,
3   Without natural affection, trucebreakers, false accusers, incontinent, fierce, despisers of those that are good,
4   Traitors, heady, highminded, lovers of pleasures more than lovers of God;
5   Having a form of godliness, but denying the power thereof: from such turn away.

Genesis 4:8–12

8   And Cain talked with Abel his brother: and it came to pass, when they were in the field, that Cain rose up against Abel his brother, and slew him.
9   And the Lord said unto Cain, Where is Abel thy brother? And he said, I know not: Am I my brother's keeper?
10   And he said, What hast thou done? the voice of thy brother's blood crieth unto me from the ground.
11   And now art thou cursed from the earth, which hath opened her mouth to receive thy brother's blood from thy hand;

12 *When thou tillest the ground, it shall not henceforth yield unto thee her strength; a fugitive and a vagabond shalt thou be in the earth.*

GENESIS 9:6

6 *Whoso sheddeth man's blood, by man shall his blood be shed: for in the image of God made he man.*

GENESIS 2:21–24

21 *And the LORD God caused a deep sleep to fall upon Adam, and he slept: and he took one of his ribs, and closed up the flesh instead thereof;*

22 *And the rib, which the LORD God had taken from man, made he a woman, and brought her unto the man.*

23 *And Adam said, This is now bone of my bones, and flesh of my flesh: she shall be called Woman, because she was taken out of Man.*

24 *Therefore shall a man leave his father and his mother, and shall cleave unto his wife: and they shall be one flesh.*

MATTHEW 19:4–6

4 *And he answered and said unto them, Have ye not read, that he which made them at the beginning made them male and female,*

5 *And said, For this cause shall a man leave father and mother, and shall cleave to his wife: and they twain shall be one flesh?*

6 *Wherefore they are no more twain, but one flesh. What therefore God hath joined together, let not man put asunder.*

GENESIS 3:19

19 *In the sweat of thy face shalt thou eat bread, till thou return unto the ground; for out of it wast thou taken: for dust thou art, and unto dust shalt thou return.*

Ephesians 4:28

28 Let him that stole steal no more: but rather let him labour, working with his hands the thing which is good, that he may have to give to him that needeth.

Matthew 6:33

33 But seek ye first the kingdom of God, and his righteousness; and all these things shall be added unto you.

2 Thessalonians 3:10–12

10 For even when we were with you, this we commanded you, that if any would not work, neither should he eat.
11 For we hear that there are some which walk among you disorderly, working not at all, but are busybodies.
12 Now them that are such we command and exhort by our Lord Jesus Christ, that with quietness they work, and eat their own bread.

John 4:24

24 God is a Spirit: and they that worship him must worship him in spirit and in truth.

Leviticus 19:11

11 Ye shall not steal, neither deal falsely, neither lie one to another.

Proverbs 10:18

18 He that hideth hatred with lying lips, and he that uttereth a slander, is a fool.

Psalm 15:1–3

1 Lord, who shall abide in thy tabernacle? who shall dwell in thy holy hill?
2 He that walketh uprightly, and worketh righteousness, and speaketh the truth in his heart.

3   He that backbiteth not with his tongue, nor doeth evil to his neighbour, nor taketh up a reproach against his neighbour.

EPHESIANS 4:31–32

31   Let all bitterness, and wrath, and anger, and clamour, and evil speaking, be put away from you, with all malice:
32   And be ye kind one to another, tenderhearted, forgiving one another, even as God for Christ's sake hath forgiven you.

LUKE 12:15–21

15   And he said unto them, Take heed, and beware of covetousness: for a man's life consisteth not in the abundance of the things which he possesseth.
16   And he spake a parable unto them, saying, The ground of a certain rich man brought forth plentifully:
17   And he thought within himself, saying, What shall I do, because I have no room where to bestow my fruits?
18   And he said, This will I do: I will pull down my barns, and build greater; and there will I bestow all my fruits and my goods.
19   And I will say to my soul, Soul, thou hast much goods laid up for many years; take thine ease, eat, drink, and be merry.
20   But God said unto him, Thou fool, this night thy soul shall be required of thee: then whose shall those things be, which thou hast provided?
21   So is he that layeth up treasure for himself, and is not rich toward God.

1 TIMOTHY 6:5–10

5   Perverse disputings of men of corrupt minds, and destitute of the truth, supposing that gain is godliness: from such withdraw thyself.

6   But godliness with contentment is great gain.

7   For we brought nothing into this world, and it is certain we can carry nothing out.

8   And having food and raiment let us be therewith content.

9   But they that will be rich fall into temptation and a snare, and into many foolish and hurtful lusts, which drown men in destruction and perdition.

10   For the love of money is the root of all evil: which while some coveted after, they have erred from the faith, and pierced themselves through with many sorrows.

III. The _____ Codes

A. The precepts were _____.

B. The promises were _____.

EXODUS 24:3, 7

3   And Moses came and told the people all the words of the LORD, and all the judgments: and all the people answered with one voice, and said, All the words which the LORD hath said will we do.

7   And he took the book of the covenant, and read in the audience of the people: and they said, All that the LORD hath said will we do, and be obedient.

Conclusion

_____

_____

_____

Study Questions

1. What pledge did God make to His people in Exodus 19?

2. What pledge did the people make to God in return?

3. How did the Lord Jesus Christ summarize the Ten Commandments?

4. List some of the topics covered in the moral precepts God gave His people in the chapters following the giving of the Ten Commandments.

5. Although we may not have bondservants or oxen today, how could we apply personally some of the moral codes found in Exodus 21–23?

6. Tell about a time God definitely blessed a specific act of obedience on your part.

7. How would we as Christians apply the commandment, "Thou shalt have no other gods before me"?

8. Why should partial obedience be considered disobedience?

Memory Verses

1 PETER 1:15–16

15 But as he which hath called you is holy, so be ye holy in all manner of conversation;
16 Because it is written, Be ye holy; for I am holy.

Moses and the Tabernacle
Living a Consecrated Life

Text

EXODUS 25:1–9

1 And the LORD spake unto Moses, saying,

2 Speak unto the children of Israel, that they bring me an offering: of every man that giveth it willingly with his heart ye shall take my offering.

3 And this is the offering which ye shall take of them; gold, and silver, and brass,

4 And blue, and purple, and scarlet, and fine linen, and goats' hair,

5 And rams' skins dyed red, and badgers' skins, and shittim wood,

6 Oil for the light, spices for anointing oil, and for sweet incense,

7 Onyx stones, and stones to be set in the ephod, and in the breastplate.

8 And let them make me a sanctuary; that I may dwell among them.

9 According to all that I shew thee, after the pattern of the tabernacle, and the pattern of all the instruments thereof, even so shall ye make it.

Overview

Having ordered the daily conduct of His people in Exodus 20–24, God now orders the worship of His people. He directed them to build a tabernacle—a dwelling place and a constant reminder of God's presence. God gave exact instructions for how the construction was to take place. Moreover, God set up a priesthood for the administration and worship of the tabernacle. He also detailed the priestly responsibilities.

In this portion of Scripture, we learn that God not only desires and deserves the worship of His people, He also directs how that worship should take place.

Introduction

_____

_____

_____

2 SAMUEL 7:1–3

1   And it came to pass, when the king sat in his house, and the LORD had given him rest round about from all his enemies;

2   That the king said unto Nathan the prophet, See now, I dwell in an house of cedar, but the ark of God dwelleth within curtains.

3   And Nathan said to the king, Go, do all that is in thine heart; for the LORD is with thee.

HAGGAI 1:3–5

3   Then came the word of the LORD by Haggai the prophet, saying,

4   Is it time for you, O ye, to dwell in your cieled houses, and this house lie waste?

5   Now therefore thus saith the LORD of hosts; Consider your ways.

I.   The Detailed _____

A.   *God told Moses* _____ *to do.*

B.   *God told Moses* _____ *to do it.*

LUKE 16:10–12

10   He that is faithful in that which is least is faithful also in much: and he that is unjust in the least is unjust also in much.

11 If therefore ye have not been faithful in the unrighteous mammon, who will commit to your trust the true riches?

12 And if ye have not been faithful in that which is another man's, who shall give you that which is your own?

II. The Delegated _____

1 PETER 2:5, 9

5 Ye also, as lively stones, are built up a spiritual house, an holy priesthood, to offer up spiritual sacrifices, acceptable to God by Jesus Christ.

9 But ye are a chosen generation, a royal priesthood, an holy nation, a peculiar people; that ye should shew forth the praises of him who hath called you out of darkness into his marvellous light:

A. The priests were _____.

ACTS 9:10–16

10 And there was a certain disciple at Damascus, named Ananias; and to him said the Lord in a vision, Ananias. And he said, Behold, I am here, Lord.

11 And the Lord said unto him, Arise, and go into the street which is called Straight, and enquire in the house of Judas for one called Saul, of Tarsus: for, behold, he prayeth,

12 And hath seen in a vision a man named Ananias coming in, and putting his hand on him, that he might receive his sight.

13 Then Ananias answered, Lord, I have heard by many of this man, how much evil he hath done to thy saints at Jerusalem:

14 And here he hath authority from the chief priests to bind all that call on thy name.

15   But the Lord said unto him, Go thy way: for he is a chosen vessel unto me, to bear my name before the Gentiles, and kings, and the children of Israel:

16   For I will shew him how great things he must suffer for my name's sake.

B.   Guidelines were given for their _____.

1 CORINTHIANS 10:31

31   Whether therefore ye eat, or drink, or whatsoever ye do, do all to the glory of God.

III. The Dedicated _____

MARK 13:1–2

1   And as he went out of the temple, one of his disciples saith unto him, Master, see what manner of stones and what buildings are here!

2   And Jesus answering said unto him, Seest thou these great buildings? there shall not be left one stone upon another, that shall not be thrown down.

A.   The _____ were consecrated.

1 CORINTHIANS 6:19–20

19   What? know ye not that your body is the temple of the Holy Ghost which is in you, which ye have of God, and ye are not your own?

20   For ye are bought with a price: therefore glorify God in your body, and in your spirit, which are God's.

ROMANS 12:1–2

1   I beseech you therefore, brethren, by the mercies of God, that ye present your bodies a living sacrifice, holy, acceptable unto God, which is your reasonable service.

2   And be not conformed to this world: but be ye transformed by the renewing of your mind, that ye may prove what is that good, and acceptable, and perfect, will of God.

B.   The _____ were consecrated.

1 PETER 1:18–19

18   Forasmuch as ye know that ye were not redeemed with corruptible things, as silver and gold, from your vain conversation received by tradition from your fathers;

19   But with the precious blood of Christ, as of a lamb without blemish and without spot:

Conclusion

_____

_____

_____

Study Questions

1. What were some of the materials God asked His people to give for the building of the tabernacle?

2. What special group did God choose for the administration of the tabernacle?

3. Whom did God choose to be the priests in the tabernacle?

4. What is the meaning of the word *consecration*?

5. What does the parable of the talents mean to you personally?

6.   Describe an incident in your life when something that seemed small made a big difference.

7.   Why should we be consecrated to God?

8.   For what purpose do you believe God has chosen you?

Memory Verse

1 CORINTHIANS 10:31
31   Whether therefore ye eat, or drink, or whatsoever ye do, do all to the glory of God.

Moses and the Golden Calf
Confession and Repentance

Text

EXODUS 32:1–14

1   And when the people saw that Moses delayed to come down out of the mount, the people gathered themselves together unto Aaron, and said unto him, Up, make us gods, which shall go before us; for as for this Moses, the man that brought us up out of the land of Egypt, we wot not what is become of him.

2   And Aaron said unto them, Break off the golden earrings, which are in the ears of your wives, of your sons, and of your daughters, and bring them unto me.

3   And all the people brake off the golden earrings which were in their ears, and brought them unto Aaron.

4   And he received them at their hand, and fashioned it with a graving tool, after he had made it a molten calf: and they said, These be thy gods, O Israel, which brought thee up out of the land of Egypt.

5   And when Aaron saw it, he built an altar before it; and Aaron made proclamation, and said, To morrow is a feast to the LORD.

6   And they rose up early on the morrow, and offered burnt offerings, and brought peace offerings; and the people sat down to eat and to drink, and rose up to play.

7   And the LORD said unto Moses, Go, get thee down; for thy people, which thou broughtest out of the land of Egypt, have corrupted themselves:

8   They have turned aside quickly out of the way which I commanded them: they have made them a molten calf, and have worshipped it, and have sacrificed thereunto, and said, These be thy gods, O Israel, which have brought thee up out of the land of Egypt.

9   And the LORD said unto Moses, I have seen this people, and, behold, it is a stiffnecked people:

10   Now therefore let me alone, that my wrath may wax hot against them, and that I may consume them: and I will make of thee a great nation.

11   And Moses besought the LORD his God, and said, LORD, why doth thy wrath wax hot against thy people, which thou hast brought forth out of the land of Egypt with great power, and with a mighty hand?

12   Wherefore should the Egyptians speak, and say, For mischief did he bring them out, to slay them in the mountains, and to consume them from the face of the earth? Turn from thy fierce wrath, and repent of this evil against thy people.

13   Remember Abraham, Isaac, and Israel, thy servants, to whom thou swarest by thine own self, and saidst unto them, I will multiply your seed as the stars of heaven, and all this land that I have spoken of will I give unto your seed, and they shall inherit it for ever.

14   And the LORD repented of the evil which he thought to do unto his people.

Overview

When people take their eyes off the true God, they are prone to the most heinous sins imaginable. God will always judge sin and deal with it severely, but the effectual fervent prayer of a righteous man will always avail much (James 5:16). One man's intercession can bring God's mercy in the midst of judgment.

Introduction

_____

_____

_____

I. The _____ of the People (vv. 1–6)

PSALM 27:14

14 *Wait on the LORD: be of good courage, and he shall strengthen thine heart: wait, I say, on the LORD.*

A. *They rebelled against _____ (vv. 1–4).*

B. *They rebelled against _____ (vv. 5–6).*

II. The _____ of God (vv. 7–10)

A. *The people were _____ (vv. 7–9).*

LUKE 24:29–32

29 *But they constrained him, saying, Abide with us: for it is toward evening, and the day is far spent. And he went in to tarry with them.*

30 *And it came to pass, as he sat at meat with them, he took bread, and blessed it, and brake, and gave to them.*

31 *And their eyes were opened, and they knew him; and he vanished out of their sight.*

32 And they said one to another, Did not our heart burn within us, while he talked with us by the way, and while he opened to us the scriptures?

EXODUS 20:4–5

4 Thou shalt not make unto thee any graven image, or any likeness of any thing that is in heaven above, or that is in the earth beneath, or that is in the water under the earth:

5 Thou shalt not bow down thyself to them, nor serve them: for I the LORD thy God am a jealous God, visiting the iniquity of the fathers upon the children unto the third and fourth generation of them that hate me;

B. **The people were _____ by God (v. 10).**

III. The _____ of Moses (vv. 11–14)

A. *He _____ the sinners (vv. 11–14).*

DEUTERONOMY 9:18–19

18 And I fell down before the LORD, as at the first, forty days and forty nights: I did neither eat bread, nor drink water, because of all your sins which ye sinned, in doing wickedly in the sight of the LORD, to provoke him to anger. 19 For I was afraid of the anger and hot displeasure, wherewith the LORD was wroth against you to destroy you. But the LORD hearkened unto me at that time also.

MATTHEW 15:22–28

22 *And, behold, a woman of Canaan came out of the same coasts, and cried unto him, saying, Have mercy on me, O Lord, thou Son of David; my daughter is grievously vexed with a devil.*

23 *But he answered her not a word. And his disciples came and besought him, saying, Send her away; for she crieth after us.*

24 *But he answered and said, I am not sent but unto the lost sheep of the house of Israel.*

25 *Then came she and worshipped him, saying, Lord, help me.*

26 *But he answered and said, It is not meet to take the children's bread, and to cast it to dogs.*

27 *And she said, Truth, Lord: yet the dogs eat of the crumbs which fall from their masters' table.*

28 *Then Jesus answered and said unto her, O woman, great is thy faith: be it unto thee even as thou wilt. And her daughter was made whole from that very hour.*

ACTS 4:13–14

13 *Now when they saw the boldness of Peter and John, and perceived that they were unlearned and ignorant men, they marvelled; and they took knowledge of them, that they had been with Jesus.*

14 *And beholding the man which was healed standing with them, they could say nothing against it.*

ACTS 27:21–25

21 *But after long abstinence Paul stood forth in the midst of them, and said, Sirs, ye should have hearkened unto me, and not have loosed from Crete, and to have gained this harm and loss.*

22 And now I exhort you to be of good cheer: for there shall be no loss of any man's life among you, but of the ship.

23 For there stood by me this night the angel of God, whose I am, and whom I serve,

24 Saying, Fear not, Paul; thou must be brought before Caesar: and, lo, God hath given thee all them that sail with thee.

25 Wherefore, sirs, be of good cheer: for I believe God, that it shall be even as it was told me.

PSALM 89:34

34 My covenant will I not break, nor alter the thing that is gone out of my lips.

NUMBERS 23:19

19 God is not a man, that he should lie; neither the son of man, that he should repent: hath he said, and shall he not do it? or hath he spoken, and shall he not make it good?

JOSHUA 23:14

14 And, behold, this day I am going the way of all the earth: and ye know in all your hearts and in all your souls, that not one thing hath failed of all the good things which the LORD your God spake concerning you; all are come to pass unto you, and not one thing hath failed thereof.

HEBREWS 4:14–16

14 Seeing then that we have a great high priest, that is passed into the heavens, Jesus the Son of God, let us hold fast our profession.

15 For we have not an high priest which cannot be touched with the feeling of our infirmities; but was in all points tempted like as we are, yet without sin.

16 Let us therefore come boldly unto the throne of grace, that we may obtain mercy, and find grace to help in time of need.

B. He _____ the sin.

NUMBERS 11:18–20, 31–33

18 And say thou unto the people, Sanctify yourselves against to morrow, and ye shall eat flesh: for ye have wept in the ears of the LORD, saying, Who shall give us flesh to eat? for it was well with us in Egypt: therefore the LORD will give you flesh, and ye shall eat.

19 Ye shall not eat one day, nor two days, nor five days, neither ten days, nor twenty days;

20 But even a whole month, until it come out at your nostrils, and it be loathsome unto you: because that ye have despised the LORD which is among you, and have wept before him, saying, Why came we forth out of Egypt?

31 And there went forth a wind from the LORD, and brought quails from the sea, and let them fall by the camp, as it were a day's journey on this side, and as it were a day's journey on the other side, round about the camp, and as it were two cubits high upon the face of the earth.

32 And the people stood up all that day, and all that night, and all the next day, and they gathered the quails: he that gathered least gathered ten homers: and they spread them all abroad for themselves round about the camp.

33 And while the flesh was yet between their teeth, ere it was chewed, the wrath of the LORD was kindled against the people, and the LORD smote the people with a very great plague.

MATTHEW 7:1–5

1 Judge not, that ye be not judged.

2   For with what judgment ye judge, ye shall be judged: and with what measure ye mete, it shall be measured to you again.

3   And why beholdest thou the mote that is in thy brother's eye, but considerest not the beam that is in thine own eye?

4   Or how wilt thou say to thy brother, Let me pull out the mote out of thine eye; and, behold, a beam is in thine own eye?

5   Thou hypocrite, first cast out the beam out of thine own eye; and then shalt thou see clearly to cast out the mote out of thy brother's eye.

Conclusion

PROVERBS 3:5–8

5   Trust in the LORD with all thine heart; and lean not unto thine own understanding.

6   In all thy ways acknowledge him, and he shall direct thy paths.

7   Be not wise in thine own eyes: fear the LORD, and depart from evil.

8   It shall be health to thy navel, and marrow to thy bones.

_____

_____

_____

Study Questions

1. What was Aaron's part in the incident of the golden calf?

2. Why did worshiping the golden calf constitute rebellion against God?

3. What two things did God tell Moses He intended to do?

4. What three things did Moses do as he interceded for his people?

5. In what ways do people engage in idolatry today?

6. If God is a merciful God, why does He have to judge and deal with our sin?

7. How can we be intercessors today?

8. What should we do before we deal with sin in others?

Memory Verses

PSALM 139:23–24
23 Search me, O God, and know my heart: try me, and know my thoughts:
24 And see if there be any wicked way in me, and lead me in the way everlasting.

Moses and His Siblings
Cultivating Family Relationships

Text

EXODUS 4:27–31

27 And the LORD said to Aaron, Go into the wilderness to meet Moses. And he went, and met him in the mount of God, and kissed him.

28 And Moses told Aaron all the words of the LORD who had sent him, and all the signs which he had commanded him.

29 And Moses and Aaron went and gathered together all the elders of the children of Israel:

30 And Aaron spake all the words which the LORD had spoken unto Moses, and did the signs in the sight of the people.

31 And the people believed: and when they heard that the LORD had visited the children of Israel, and that he had looked upon their affliction, then they bowed their heads and worshipped.

Overview

Relationships with family members can be a great blessing, but we all know they can be problematic at times, too! We do not choose our parents, siblings, children, or extended family members, but God has chosen them for us. So, we must trust His sovereign plan and seek to draw our loved ones closer to Him.

Introduction

_____

_____

_____

I. Moses and _____

A. Miriam _____.

EXODUS 2:1–8

1   And there went a man of the house of Levi, and took to wife a daughter of Levi.

2   And the woman conceived, and bare a son: and when she saw him that he was a goodly child, she hid him three months.

3   And when she could not longer hide him, she took for him an ark of bulrushes, and daubed it with slime and with pitch, and put the child therein; and she laid it in the flags by the river's brink.

4   And his sister stood afar off, to wit what would be done to him.

5   And the daughter of Pharaoh came down to wash herself at the river; and her maidens walked along by the river's side; and when she saw the ark among the flags, she sent her maid to fetch it.

6   And when she had opened it, she saw the child: and, behold, the babe wept. And she had compassion on him, and said, This is one of the Hebrews' children.

7   Then said his sister to Pharaoh's daughter, Shall I go and call to thee a nurse of the Hebrew women, that she may nurse the child for thee?

8   And Pharaoh's daughter said to her, Go. And the maid went and called the child's mother.

EXODUS 15:20–21

20   And Miriam the prophetess, the sister of Aaron, took a timbrel in her hand; and all the women went out after her with timbrels and with dances.

21   And Miriam answered them, Sing ye to the LORD, for he hath triumphed gloriously; the horse and his rider hath he thrown into the sea.

ROMANS 16:1–9

1   I commend unto you Phebe our sister, which is a servant of the church which is at Cenchrea:

2   That ye receive her in the Lord, as becometh saints, and that ye assist her in whatsoever business she hath need of you: for she hath been a succourer of many, and of myself also.

3   Greet Priscilla and Aquila my helpers in Christ Jesus:

4   Who have for my life laid down their own necks: unto whom not only I give thanks, but also all the churches of the Gentiles.

5   Likewise greet the church that is in their house. Salute my wellbeloved Epaenetus, who is the firstfruits of Achaia unto Christ.

6   Greet Mary, who bestowed much labour on us.

7   Salute Andronicus and Junia, my kinsmen, and my fellowprisoners, who are of note among the apostles, who also were in Christ before me.

8   Greet Amplias my beloved in the Lord.

9   Salute Urbane, our helper in Christ, and Stachys my beloved.

B. Miriam _____.

NUMBERS 12:1–5

1   And Miriam and Aaron spake against Moses because of the Ethiopian woman whom he had married: for he had married an Ethiopian woman.

2   And they said, Hath the LORD indeed spoken only by Moses? hath he not spoken also by us? And the LORD heard it.

3   (Now the man Moses was very meek, above all the men which were upon the face of the earth.)

4   And the LORD spake suddenly unto Moses, and unto Aaron, and unto Miriam, Come out ye three unto the tabernacle of the congregation. And they three came out.

5   And the LORD came down in the pillar of the cloud, and stood in the door of the tabernacle, and called Aaron and Miriam: and they both came forth.

II. Moses and _____

A. Aaron _____.

EXODUS 4:13–16

13   And he said, O my Lord, send, I pray thee, by the hand of him whom thou wilt send.

14   And the anger of the LORD was kindled against Moses, and he said, Is not Aaron the Levite thy brother? I know that he can speak well. And also, behold, he cometh forth to meet thee: and when he seeth thee, he will be glad in his heart.

15   And thou shalt speak unto him, and put words in his mouth: and I will be with thy mouth, and with his mouth, and will teach you what ye shall do.

16 *And he shall be thy spokesman unto the people: and he shall be, even he shall be to thee instead of a mouth, and thou shalt be to him instead of God.*

EXODUS 5:1–3

1 *And afterward Moses and Aaron went in, and told Pharaoh, Thus saith the LORD God of Israel, Let my people go, that they may hold a feast unto me in the wilderness.*

2 *And Pharaoh said, Who is the LORD, that I should obey his voice to let Israel go? I know not the LORD, neither will I let Israel go.*

3 *And they said, The God of the Hebrews hath met with us: let us go, we pray thee, three days' journey into the desert, and sacrifice unto the LORD our God; lest he fall upon us with pestilence, or with the sword.*

EXODUS 28:1

1 *And take thou unto thee Aaron thy brother, and his sons with him, from among the children of Israel, that he may minister unto me in the priest's office, even Aaron, Nadab and Abihu, Eleazar and Ithamar, Aaron's sons.*

B. Aaron _____.

1 SAMUEL 12:24

24 *Only fear the LORD, and serve him in truth with all your heart: for consider how great things he hath done for you.*

ROMANS 12:1

1 *I beseech you therefore, brethren, by the mercies of God, that ye present your bodies a living sacrifice, holy, acceptable unto God, which is your reasonable service.*

Romans 2:4

4   Or despisest thou the riches of his goodness and forbearance and longsuffering; not knowing that the goodness of God leadeth thee to repentance?

Psalm 116:12–14

12   What shall I render unto the Lord for all his benefits toward me?

13   I will take the cup of salvation, and call upon the name of the Lord.

14   I will pay my vows unto the Lord now in the presence of all his people.

Titus 3:3–8

3   For we ourselves also were sometimes foolish, disobedient, deceived, serving divers lusts and pleasures, living in malice and envy, hateful, and hating one another.

4   But after that the kindness and love of God our Saviour toward man appeared,

5   Not by works of righteousness which we have done, but according to his mercy he saved us, by the washing of regeneration, and renewing of the Holy Ghost;

6   Which he shed on us abundantly through Jesus Christ our Saviour;

7   That being justified by his grace, we should be made heirs according to the hope of eternal life.

8   This is a faithful saying, and these things I will that thou affirm constantly, that they which have believed in God might be careful to maintain good works. These things are good and profitable unto men.

1 John 4:19

19   We love him, because he first loved us.

III. Moses and _____

NUMBERS 12:3

3 *(Now the man Moses was very meek, above all the men which were upon the face of the earth.)*

2 PETER 3:9

9 *The Lord is not slack concerning his promise, as some men count slackness; but is longsuffering to us-ward, not willing that any should perish, but that all should come to repentance.*

EPHESIANS 4:32

32 *And be ye kind one to another, tenderhearted, forgiving one another, even as God for Christ's sake hath forgiven you.*

A. Moses _____.

NUMBERS 20:1, 12, 23–29

1 *Then came the children of Israel, even the whole congregation, into the desert of Zin in the first month: and the people abode in Kadesh; and Miriam died there, and was buried there.*

12 *And the LORD spake unto Moses and Aaron, Because ye believed me not, to sanctify me in the eyes of the children of Israel, therefore ye shall not bring this congregation into the land which I have given them.*

23 *And the LORD spake unto Moses and Aaron in mount Hor, by the coast of the land of Edom, saying,*

24 *Aaron shall be gathered unto his people: for he shall not enter into the land which I have given unto the children of Israel, because ye rebelled against my word at the water of Meribah.*

25 *Take Aaron and Eleazar his son, and bring them up unto mount Hor:*

26 And strip Aaron of his garments, and put them upon Eleazar his son: and Aaron shall be gathered unto his people, and shall die there.

27 And Moses did as the LORD commanded: and they went up into mount Hor in the sight of all the congregation.

28 And Moses stripped Aaron of his garments, and put them upon Eleazar his son; and Aaron died there in the top of the mount: and Moses and Eleazar came down from the mount.

29 And when all the congregation saw that Aaron was dead, they mourned for Aaron thirty days, even all the house of Israel.

DEUTERONOMY 32:29

29 O that they were wise, that they understood this, that they would consider their latter end!

B. Moses _____.

Conclusion

_____

_____

_____

Study Questions

1. What part did Miriam play in the early life of Moses?

2. How should Miriam have handled Moses' marriage to the Ethiopian woman?

3. How did Aaron support Moses as they confronted Pharaoh?

4. How did Aaron show disrespect to Moses in the matter of the golden calf?

5. How should we handle it when we disagree with our spiritual leader or leaders?

6. What can we do to support our earthly brothers and sisters in the Lord?

7. What do we mean by "thinkfulness will lead to thankfulness"?

8. Tell about a time you exercised longsuffering when you were tempted to do otherwise.

Memory Verse

EPHESIANS 4:32

32 *And be ye kind one to another, tenderhearted, forgiving one another, even as God for Christ's sake hath forgiven you.*

Moses and the Wilderness Wanderings
Leading Others

Text

NUMBERS 13:1–33

1   And the LORD spake unto Moses, saying,

2   Send thou men, that they may search the land of Canaan, which I give unto the children of Israel: of every tribe of their fathers shall ye send a man, every one a ruler among them.

3   And Moses by the commandment of the LORD sent them from the wilderness of Paran: all those men were heads of the children of Israel.

4   And these were their names: of the tribe of Reuben, Shammua the son of Zaccur.

5   Of the tribe of Simeon, Shaphat the son of Hori.

6   Of the tribe of Judah, Caleb the son of Jephunneh.

7   Of the tribe of Issachar, Igal the son of Joseph.

8   Of the tribe of Ephraim, Oshea the son of Nun.

9   Of the tribe of Benjamin, Palti the son of Raphu.

10   Of the tribe of Zebulun, Gaddiel the son of Sodi.

11   Of the tribe of Joseph, namely, of the tribe of Manasseh, Gaddi the son of Susi.

12   Of the tribe of Dan, Ammiel the son of Gemalli.

13   Of the tribe of Asher, Sethur the son of Michael.

14   Of the tribe of Naphtali, Nahbi the son of Vophsi.

15   Of the tribe of Gad, Geuel the son of Machi.

16   These are the names of the men which Moses sent to spy out the land. And Moses called Oshea the son of Nun Jehoshua.

17   And Moses sent them to spy out the land of Canaan, and said unto them, Get you up this way southward, and go up into the mountain:

18   And see the land, what it is; and the people that dwelleth therein, whether they be strong or weak, few or many;

19   And what the land is that they dwell in, whether it be good or bad; and what cities they be that they dwell in, whether in tents, or in strong holds;

20   And what the land is, whether it be fat or lean, whether there be wood therein, or not. And be ye of good courage, and bring of the fruit of the land. Now the time was the time of the firstripe grapes.

21   So they went up, and searched the land from the wilderness of Zin unto Rehob, as men come to Hamath.

22   And they ascended by the south, and came unto Hebron; where Ahiman, Sheshai, and Talmai, the children of Anak, were. (Now Hebron was built seven years before Zoan in Egypt.)

23   And they came unto the brook of Eshcol, and cut down from thence a branch with one cluster of grapes, and they bare it between two upon a staff; and they brought of the pomegranates, and of the figs.

24   The place was called the brook Eshcol, because of the cluster of grapes which the children of Israel cut down from thence.

25   And they returned from searching of the land after forty days.

26   And they went and came to Moses, and to Aaron, and to all the congregation of the children of Israel, unto the wilderness of Paran, to Kadesh; and brought back word unto them, and unto all the congregation, and shewed them the fruit of the land.

27   And they told him, and said, We came unto the land whither thou sentest us, and surely it floweth with milk and honey; and this is the fruit of it.

28 Nevertheless the people be strong that dwell in the land, and the cities are walled, and very great: and moreover we saw the children of Anak there.

29 The Amalekites dwell in the land of the south: and the Hittites, and the Jebusites, and the Amorites, dwell in the mountains: and the Canaanites dwell by the sea, and by the coast of Jordan.

30 And Caleb stilled the people before Moses, and said, Let us go up at once, and possess it; for we are well able to overcome it.

31 But the men that went up with him said, We be not able to go up against the people; for they are stronger than we.

32 And they brought up an evil report of the land which they had searched unto the children of Israel, saying, The land, through which we have gone to search it, is a land that eateth up the inhabitants thereof; and all the people that we saw in it are men of a great stature.

33 And there we saw the giants, the sons of Anak, which come of the giants: and we were in our own sight as grasshoppers, and so we were in their sight.

Overview

Trusting and following God is a course that must be actively chosen. Often it is not the easy or most convenient way, nor is it the way that looks the most promising to the unspiritual eye. Yet it is in faith-filled obedience that we triumph over obstacles and enter into "the things which God hath prepared for them that love him" (1 Corinthians 2:9). When we walk by sight, we forfeit the benefits of walking by faith.

Introduction

_____

_____

_____

I. The _____ of the Spies

A. *The spies _____ the land.*

B. *The spies _____ their recommendations.*

EXODUS 3:7–8

7   And the LORD said, I have surely seen the affliction of my people which are in Egypt, and have heard their cry by reason of their taskmasters; for I know their sorrows;

8   And I am come down to deliver them out of the hand of the Egyptians, and to bring them up out of that land unto a good land and a large, unto a land flowing with milk and honey; unto the place of the Canaanites, and the Hittites, and the Amorites, and the Perizzites, and the Hivites, and the Jebusites.

MATTHEW 16:18

18   And I say also unto thee, That thou art Peter, and upon this rock I will build my church; and the gates of hell shall not prevail against it.

1 JOHN 4:4

4 Ye are of God, little children, and have overcome them: because greater is he that is in you, than he that is in the world.

2 TIMOTHY 1:7

7   For God hath not given us the spirit of fear; but of power, and of love, and of a sound mind.

PHILIPPIANS 4:13

13   I can do all things through Christ which strengtheneth me.

MATTHEW 14:25–32

25   And in the fourth watch of the night Jesus went unto them, walking on the sea.

26   And when the disciples saw him walking on the sea, they were troubled, saying, It is a spirit; and they cried out for fear.

27   But straightway Jesus spake unto them, saying, Be of good cheer; it is I; be not afraid.

28   And Peter answered him and said, Lord, if it be thou, bid me come unto thee on the water.

29   And he said, Come. And when Peter was come down out of the ship, he walked on the water, to go to Jesus.

30   But when he saw the wind boisterous, he was afraid; and beginning to sink, he cried, saying, Lord, save me.

31   And immediately Jesus stretched forth his hand, and caught him, and said unto him, O thou of little faith, wherefore didst thou doubt?

32   And when they were come into the ship, the wind ceased.

II. The _____ of the People

ROMANS 14:19

19   Let us therefore follow after the things which make for peace, and things wherewith one may edify another.

A. The people _____.

NUMBERS 14:1–4

1 And all the congregation lifted up their voice, and cried; and the people wept that night.

2 And all the children of Israel murmured against Moses and against Aaron: and the whole congregation said unto them, Would God that we had died in the land of Egypt! or would God we had died in this wilderness!

3 And wherefore hath the LORD brought us unto this land, to fall by the sword, that our wives and our children should be a prey? were it not better for us to return into Egypt?

4 And they said one to another, Let us make a captain, and let us return into Egypt.

B. The people _____.

NUMBERS 14:10

10 But all the congregation bade stone them with stones. And the glory of the LORD appeared in the tabernacle of the congregation before all the children of Israel.

ACTS 17:32–34

32 And when they heard of the resurrection of the dead, some mocked: and others said, We will hear thee again of this matter.

33 So Paul departed from among them.

34 Howbeit certain men clave unto him, and believed: among the which was Dionysius the Areopagite, and a woman named Damaris, and others with them.

III. The _____ of God

A. *God gave a* _____.

NUMBERS 14:11–12, 22–24, 28–35

11 And the LORD said unto Moses, How long will this people provoke me? and how long will it be ere they believe me, for all the signs which I have shewed among them?

12 I will smite them with the pestilence, and disinherit them, and will make of thee a greater nation and mightier than they.

22 Because all those men which have seen my glory, and my miracles, which I did in Egypt and in the wilderness, and have tempted me now these ten times, and have not hearkened to my voice;

23 Surely they shall not see the land which I sware unto their fathers, neither shall any of them that provoked me see it:

24 But my servant Caleb, because he had another spirit with him, and hath followed me fully, him will I bring into the land whereinto he went; and his seed shall possess it.

28 Say unto them, As truly as I live, saith the LORD, as ye have spoken in mine ears, so will I do to you:

29 Your carcases shall fall in this wilderness; and all that were numbered of you, according to your whole number, from twenty years old and upward, which have murmured against me,

30 Doubtless ye shall not come into the land, concerning which I sware to make you dwell therein, save Caleb the son of Jephunneh, and Joshua the son of Nun.

31 But your little ones, which ye said should be a prey, them will I bring in, and they shall know the land which ye have despised.

32 But as for you, your carcases, they shall fall in this wilderness.

33 And your children shall wander in the wilderness forty years, and bear your whoredoms, until your carcases be wasted in the wilderness.

34 After the number of the days in which ye searched the land, even forty days, each day for a year, shall ye bear your iniquities, even forty years, and ye shall know my breach of promise.

35 I the LORD have said, I will surely do it unto all this evil congregation, that are gathered together against me: in this wilderness they shall be consumed, and there they shall die.

PROVERBS 13:15

15 Good understanding giveth favour: but the way of transgressors is hard.

JAMES 1:15

15 Then when lust hath conceived, it bringeth forth sin: and sin, when it is finished, bringeth forth death.

2 CHRONICLES 36:15–20

15 And the LORD God of their fathers sent to them by his messengers, rising up betimes, and sending; because he had compassion on his people, and on his dwelling place:

16 But they mocked the messengers of God, and despised his words, and misused his prophets, until the wrath of the LORD arose against his people, till there was no remedy.

17 Therefore he brought upon them the king of the Chaldees, who slew their young men with the sword in the house of their sanctuary, and had no compassion upon young man or maiden, old man, or him that stooped for age: he gave them all into his hand.

18 And all the vessels of the house of God, great and small, and the treasures of the house of the LORD, and the treasures of the king, and of his princes; all these he brought to Babylon.
19 And they burnt the house of God, and brake down the wall of Jerusalem, and burnt all the palaces thereof with fire, and destroyed all the goodly vessels thereof.
20 And them that had escaped from the sword carried he away to Babylon; where they were servants to him and his sons until the reign of the kingdom of Persia:

B. God promised His _____ care.

NUMBERS 14:20, 30–31
20 And the LORD said, I have pardoned according to thy word:
30 Doubtless ye shall not come into the land, concerning which I sware to make you dwell therein, save Caleb the son of Jephunneh, and Joshua the son of Nun.
31 But your little ones, which ye said should be a prey, them will I bring in, and they shall know the land which ye have despised.

PSALM 103:10
10 He hath not dealt with us after our sins; nor rewarded us according to our iniquities.

DEUTERONOMY 29:5
5 And I have led you forty years in the wilderness: your clothes are not waxen old upon you, and thy shoe is not waxen old upon thy foot.

NEHEMIAH 9:18–21
18 Yea, when they had made them a molten calf, and said, This is thy God that brought thee up out of Egypt, and had wrought great provocations;

19 *Yet thou in thy manifold mercies forsookest them not in the wilderness: the pillar of the cloud departed not from them by day, to lead them in the way; neither the pillar of fire by night, to shew them light, and the way wherein they should go.*

20 *Thou gavest also thy good spirit to instruct them, and withheldest not thy manna from their mouth, and gavest them water for their thirst.*

21 *Yea, forty years didst thou sustain them in the wilderness, so that they lacked nothing; their clothes waxed not old, and their feet swelled not.*

LAMENTATIONS 3:21–26

21 *This I recall to my mind, therefore have I hope.*

22 *It is of the LORD's mercies that we are not consumed, because his compassions fail not.*

23 *They are new every morning: great is thy faithfulness.*

24 *The LORD is my portion, saith my soul; therefore will I hope in him.*

25 *The LORD is good unto them that wait for him, to the soul that seeketh him.*

26 *It is good that a man should both hope and quietly wait for the salvation of the LORD.*

Conclusion

2 CHRONICLES 16:9

9 *For the eyes of the LORD run to and fro throughout the whole earth, to shew himself strong in the behalf of them whose heart is perfect toward him....*

_____

_____

_____

Study Questions

1. For what purpose did Moses send the spies into the Promised Land?

2. What did the spies see during their time in the Promised Land?

3. What was the recommendation of the ten pessimistic spies? What did Joshua and Caleb have to say?

4. What did the people want to do, and how did God respond?

5. How should we respond when circumstances look too difficult for us to handle?

6. Give an example of a time you chose faith over fear. What was the result?

7. Give an example of a time you chose fear over faith. What was the result?

8. Give an example of how God has been better to you than you deserve.

Memory Verse

PROVERBS 13:15
15 *Good understanding giveth favour: but the way of transgressors is hard.*

Moses and His Approaching Death
Leaving a Spiritual Legacy

Text

DEUTERONOMY 31:1–9

1   *And Moses went and spake these words unto all Israel.*

2   *And he said unto them, I am an hundred and twenty years old this day; I can no more go out and come in: also the LORD hath said unto me, Thou shalt not go over this Jordan.*

3   *The LORD thy God, he will go over before thee, and he will destroy these nations from before thee, and thou shalt possess them: and Joshua, he shall go over before thee, as the LORD hath said.*

4   *And the LORD shall do unto them as he did to Sihon and to Og, kings of the Amorites, and unto the land of them, whom he destroyed.*

5   *And the LORD shall give them up before your face, that ye may do unto them according unto all the commandments which I have commanded you.*

6   *Be strong and of a good courage, fear not, nor be afraid of them: for the LORD thy God, he it is that doth go with thee; he will not fail thee, nor forsake thee.*

7   *And Moses called unto Joshua, and said unto him in the sight of all Israel, Be strong and of a good courage: for thou must go with this people unto the land which the LORD hath sworn unto their fathers to give them; and thou shalt cause them to inherit it.*

8   *And the LORD, he it is that doth go before thee; he will be with thee, he will not fail thee, neither forsake thee: fear not, neither be dismayed.*

9   *And Moses wrote this law, and delivered it unto the priests the sons of Levi, which bare the ark of the covenant of the* Lord, *and unto all the elders of Israel.*

Overview

When we come to realize that our time is in God's hand, we begin to understand what is truly important in life. Our own relationship with God and the spiritual well-being of those we may leave behind come to the forefront of our thinking. So the awareness that the Lord could call us home to Heaven at any moment should prompt us to be prepared to go.

Introduction

_____

_____

_____

I. God's Covenant with _____

1 TIMOTHY 2:5
5 *For there is one God, and one mediator between God and men, the man Christ Jesus;*

HEBREWS 8:6
6 *But now hath he obtained a more excellent ministry, by how much also he is the mediator of a better covenant, which was established upon better promises.*

HEBREWS 9:15
15 *And for this cause he is the mediator of the new testament, that by means of death, for the redemption of the transgressions that were under the first testament, they which are called might receive the promise of eternal inheritance.*

HEBREWS 12:24
24 *And to Jesus the mediator of the new covenant, and to the blood of sprinkling, that speaketh better things than that of Abel.*

A. *Moses reminded them of God's* _____.

DEUTERONOMY 29:9
9 *Keep therefore the words of this covenant, and do them, that ye may prosper in all that ye do.*

DEUTERONOMY 5:1
1   And Moses called all Israel, and said unto them, Hear, O Israel, the statutes and judgments which I speak in your ears this day, that ye may learn them, and keep, and do them.

DEUTERONOMY 6:4
4   Hear, O Israel: The LORD our God is one LORD:

DEUTERONOMY 9:1
1   Hear, O Israel: Thou art to pass over Jordan this day, to go in to possess nations greater and mightier than thyself, cities great and fenced up to heaven,

DEUTERONOMY 20:3
3   And shall say unto them, Hear, O Israel, ye approach this day unto battle against your enemies: let not your hearts faint, fear not, and do not tremble, neither be ye terrified because of them;

DEUTERONOMY 32:1
1   Give ear, O ye heavens, and I will speak; and hear, O earth, the words of my mouth.

PROVERBS 1:5, 8
5   A wise man will hear, and will increase learning; and a man of understanding shall attain unto wise counsels:
8   My son, hear the instruction of thy father, and forsake not the law of thy mother:

MARK 12:29
29 And Jesus answered him, The first of all the commandments is, Hear, O Israel; The Lord our God is one Lord:

JAMES 1:22–25

22 *But be ye doers of the word, and not hearers only, deceiving your own selves.*

23 *For if any be a hearer of the word, and not a doer, he is like unto a man beholding his natural face in a glass:*

24 *For he beholdeth himself, and goeth his way, and straightway forgetteth what manner of man he was.*

25 *But whoso looketh into the perfect law of liberty, and continueth therein, he being not a forgetful hearer, but a doer of the work, this man shall be blessed in his deed.*

B. Moses reminded them of their _____.

GALATIANS 6:7–9

7 *Be not deceived; God is not mocked: for whatsoever a man soweth, that shall he also reap.*

8 *For he that soweth to his flesh shall of the flesh reap corruption; but he that soweth to the Spirit shall of the Spirit reap life everlasting.*

9 *And let us not be weary in well doing: for in due season we shall reap, if we faint not.*

1 CORINTHIANS 15:58

58 *Therefore, my beloved brethren, be ye stedfast, unmoveable, always abounding in the work of the Lord, forasmuch as ye know that your labour is not in vain in the Lord.*

DEUTERONOMY 32:35

35 *To me belongeth vengeance, and recompence; their foot shall slide in due time: for the day of their calamity is at hand, and the things that shall come upon them make haste.*

PSALM 73:12–19

12 Behold, these are the ungodly, who prosper in the world; they increase in riches.

13 Verily I have cleansed my heart in vain, and washed my hands in innocency.

14 For all the day long have I been plagued, and chastened every morning.

15 If I say, I will speak thus; behold, I should offend against the generation of thy children.

16 When I thought to know this, it was too painful for me;

17 Until I went into the sanctuary of God; then understood I their end.

18 Surely thou didst set them in slippery places: thou castedst them down into destruction.

19 How are they brought into desolation, as in a moment! they are utterly consumed with terrors.

JAMES 1:5

5 If any of you lack wisdom, let him ask of God, that giveth to all men liberally, and upbraideth not; and it shall be given him.

PROVERBS 3:5–6

5 Trust in the LORD with all thine heart; and lean not unto thine own understanding.

6 In all thy ways acknowledge him, and he shall direct thy paths.

II. God's Charge to _____

A. He was to look _____ in courage.

DEUTERONOMY 31:1, 6–7, 23

1   *And Moses went and spake these words unto all Israel.*

6   *Be strong and of a good courage, fear not, nor be afraid of them: for the LORD thy God, he it is that doth go with thee; he will not fail thee, nor forsake thee.*

7   *And Moses called unto Joshua, and said unto him in the sight of all Israel, Be strong and of a good courage: for thou must go with this people unto the land which the LORD hath sworn unto their fathers to give them; and thou shalt cause them to inherit it.*

23   *And he gave Joshua the son of Nun a charge, and said, Be strong and of a good courage: for thou shalt bring the children of Israel into the land which I sware unto them: and I will be with thee.*

ACTS 2:41–47

41   *Then they that gladly received his word were baptized: and the same day there were added unto them about three thousand souls.*

42   *And they continued stedfastly in the apostles' doctrine and fellowship, and in breaking of bread, and in prayers.*

43   *And fear came upon every soul: and many wonders and signs were done by the apostles.*

44   *And all that believed were together, and had all things common;*

45   *And sold their possessions and goods, and parted them to all men, as every man had need.*

46   *And they, continuing daily with one accord in the temple, and breaking bread from house to house, did eat their meat with gladness and singleness of heart,*

47   *Praising God, and having favour with all the people. And the Lord added to the church daily such as should be saved.*

JOSHUA 1:6–9

6 Be strong and of a good courage: for unto this people shalt thou divide for an inheritance the land, which I sware unto their fathers to give them.

7 Only be thou strong and very courageous, that thou mayest observe to do according to all the law, which Moses my servant commanded thee: turn not from it to the right hand or to the left, that thou mayest prosper whithersoever thou goest.

8 This book of the law shall not depart out of thy mouth; but thou shalt meditate therein day and night, that thou mayest observe to do according to all that is written therein: for then thou shalt make thy way prosperous, and then thou shalt have good success.

9 Have not I commanded thee? Be strong and of a good courage; be not afraid, neither be thou dismayed: for the LORD thy God is with thee whithersoever thou goest.

DEUTERONOMY 2:30

30 But Sihon king of Heshbon would not let us pass by him: for the LORD thy God hardened his spirit, and made his heart obstinate, that he might deliver him into thy hand, as appeareth this day.

DEUTERONOMY 15:7

7 If there be among you a poor man of one of thy brethren within any of thy gates in thy land which the LORD thy God giveth thee, thou shalt not harden thine heart, nor shut thine hand from thy poor brother:

PROVERBS 24:5

5 A wise man is strong; yea, a man of knowledge increaseth strength.

ISAIAH 35:3

3   Strengthen ye the weak hands, and confirm the feeble knees.

B. He was to look _____
    in commemoration.

DEUTERONOMY 32:7

7   Remember the days of old, consider the years of many generations: ask thy father, and he will shew thee; thy elders, and they will tell thee.

DEUTERONOMY 32:10

10   He found him in a desert land, and in the waste howling wilderness; he led him about, he instructed him, he kept him as the apple of his eye.

ISAIAH 57:15

15   For thus saith the high and lofty One that inhabiteth eternity, whose name is Holy; I dwell in the high and holy place, with him also that is of a contrite and humble spirit, to revive the spirit of the humble, and to revive the heart of the contrite ones.

2 PETER 3:8

8   But, beloved, be not ignorant of this one thing, that one day is with the Lord as a thousand years, and a thousand years as one day.

PSALM 31:15

15   My times are in thy hand: deliver me from the hand of mine enemies, and from them that persecute me.

III. God's Care for _____ and the _____

A. *The tribes were _____ blessed.*

JAMES 1:17

17 Every good gift and every perfect gift is from above, and cometh down from the Father of lights, with whom is no variableness, neither shadow of turning.

1 CORINTHIANS 2:9

9 But as it is written, Eye hath not seen, nor ear heard, neither have entered into the heart of man, the things which God hath prepared for them that love him.

ISAIAH 59:1–2

1 Behold, the LORD's hand is not shortened, that it cannot save; neither his ear heavy, that it cannot hear:
2 But your iniquities have separated between you and your God, and your sins have hid his face from you, that he will not hear.

LUKE 13:34

34 O Jerusalem, Jerusalem, which killest the prophets, and stonest them that are sent unto thee; how often would I have gathered thy children together, as a hen doth gather her brood under her wings, and ye would not!

B. *Moses was _____ buried.*

DEUTERONOMY 34:5–8

5 So Moses the servant of the LORD died there in the land of Moab, according to the word of the LORD.

6   And he buried him in a valley in the land of Moab, over against Bethpeor: but no man knoweth of his sepulchre unto this day.

7   And Moses was an hundred and twenty years old when he died: his eye was not dim, nor his natural force abated.

8   And the children of Israel wept for Moses in the plains of Moab thirty days: so the days of weeping and mourning for Moses were ended.

Conclusion

DEUTERONOMY 34:10–12

10   And there arose not a prophet since in Israel like unto Moses, whom the LORD knew face to face,

11   In all the signs and the wonders, which the LORD sent him to do in the land of Egypt to Pharaoh, and to all his servants, and to all his land,

12   And in all that mighty hand, and in all the great terror which Moses shewed in the sight of all Israel.

_____

_____

_____

Study Questions

1. What is meant by the word *covenant*?

2. What were the choices God gave His people in Deuteronomy 30?

3. What was the charge Moses gave Joshua in Deuteronomy 31?

4. Describe the homegoing of Moses and the reaction of his people (Deuteronomy 34).

5. What is the basis of our covenant with God?

6. What is the basis of our strength and courage as Christians?

7. To whom do you need to express your appreciation today before they depart from this life?

8. What elements of Moses' character mean the most to you, and which would you most like to emulate?

Memory Verses

PROVERBS 3:5–6

5   *Trust in the LORD with all thine heart; and lean not unto thine own understanding.*
6   *In all thy ways acknowledge him, and he shall direct thy paths.*

For additional Christian
growth resources visit
strivingtogether.com